نَحْنُ كُلُّنا مُتَشابِهون

نَحْنُ كُلُّنا مُخْتَلِفون

Photographs: Cover and p. 9: James Levin/SODA; Cover and p. 6: James Levin/Studio 10/SODA;
p. 12: Digital Vision/Getty Images; p. 16: Richard Hutchings via SODA ; p. 17: Photodisc via SODA;
p. 23: Xavier Bonghi/The Image Bank/Getty Images; p. 29: James Levin/SODA;

Photographs copyright © 1991 by Laura Dwight.
Copyright © 1991 by Scholastic Inc. All rights reserved.
Published by Scholastic Inc. SCHOLASTIC and associated logos
are trademarks and/or registered trademarks of Scholastic Inc.

Designed by Leslie Bauman

ISBN 978-0-439-86536-4

First Arabic Edition, 2006. Printed in China.

1 2 3 4 5 6 7 8 9 10 62 09 08 07

نَحْنُ كُلُّنا مُتَّشابِهونَ
نَحْنُ كُلُّنا مُخْتَلِفونَ

تَأْليفُ وَرُسومُ:
الْمَدارِسُ الْإِبْتِدائِيَّةُ،
وَرِياضُ الْأَطْفالِ.

نَحْنُ كُلُّنا مُتَشابِهونَ.
كُلُّنا بَشَرٌ.

نَحْنُ كُلُّنا مُخْتَلِفونَ.

مَظْهَرُنا الْخارِجِيُّ مُخْتَلِفٌ.

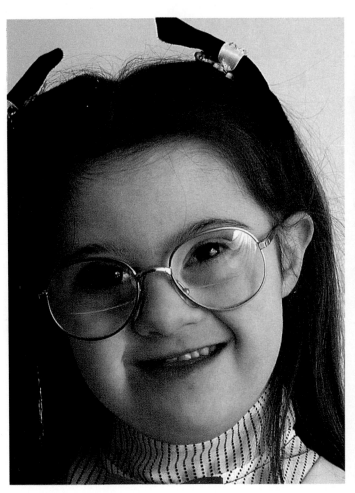

أَلْوانُ عُيونِنا مُخْتَلِفَةٌ.

أَلْوانُ شُعورِنا مُخْتَلِفَةٌ.

شَعْرُ بَعْضِنا أَجْعَدُ.

شَعْرُ بَعْضِنا أَمْلَسُ.

وَبَعْضُنا يَضَعُ نَظّاراتٍ.

أَلْوانُ بَشَراتِنا مُخْتَلِفَةٌ.

بَعْضُنا لَهُ بَشَرَةٌ غامِقَةٌ.

وَبَعْضُنا لَهُ بَشَرَةٌ فاتِحَةٌ.

ما لَوْنُ شَعْرِكَ، وَبَشَرَتِكَ، وَعَيْنَيْكَ؟

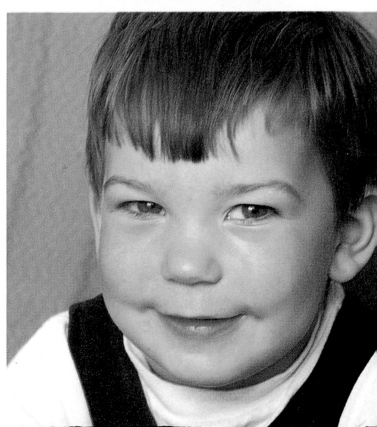

نَحْنُ كُلُّنا مُتَشابِهونَ.
كُلُّنا يَمْلِكُ أَجْسامًا.

نَحْنُ كُلُّنا مُخْتَلِفونَ.

بَعْضُنا فَتياتٌ.

وَبَعْضُنا فِتيانٌ.

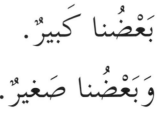

بَعْضُنا كَبيرٌ.
وَبَعْضُنا صَغيرٌ.

كَيْفَ هُوَ شَكْلُ جِسْمِكَ؟

نَحْنُ كُلُّنا مُتَشابِهونَ.
كُلُّنا لَهُ عائِلاتٌ.

كُلُّنا مُخْتَلِفونَ.

بَعْضُنا يَتيمُ الأَبِ، وَيَعيشُ مَعَ أُمِّهِ.

بَعْضُنا يَتيمُ الأُمِّ، وَيَعيشُ مَعَ أَبيهِ.

وَبَعْضُنا يَعيشُ مَعَ أُمِّهِ وَأَبيهِ.

بَعْضُنا يَعيشُ مَعَ جَدِّهِ وَجَدَّتِهِ.

وَبَعْضُنا يَعيشُ مَعَ إِخْوَتِهِ وَأَخَواتِهِ.

بَعْضُنا يُشْبِهُ أُمَّهُ، أَوْ أَباهُ.
بَعْضُنا لا يُشْبِهُ أُمَّهُ، وَلا أَباهُ.

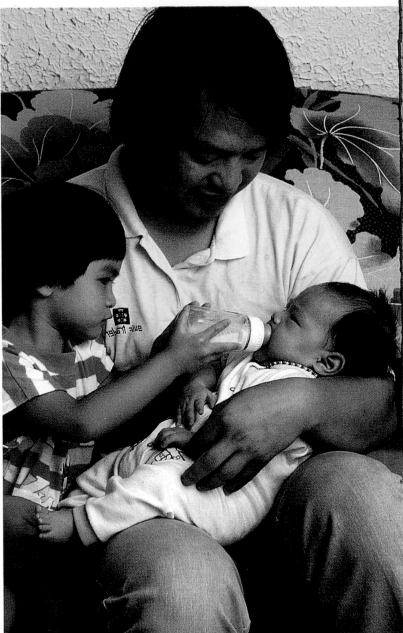

ما أَشْكالُ أَفْرادِ عائِلَتِكَ الْخارِجِيَّةُ؟

نَحْنُ كُلُّنا مُتَشابِهونَ.
كُلُّنا يَعيشُ في مَكانٍ ما.

نَحْنُ كُلُّنا مُخْتَلِفونَ.

بَعْضُنا يَعيشُ في الْمَدينَةِ.

بَعْضُنا يَعيشُ في الرّيفِ.

بَعْضُنا يَعيشُ في شِقَقٍ.

بَعْضُنا يَعيشُ في بُيوتٍ.

وَبَعْضُنا يَعيشُ في مَقْطوراتٍ.

أَيْنَ تَسْكُنُ؟

نَحْنُ كُلُّنا مُتَشابِهونَ.
كُلُّنا يَأْكُلُ.

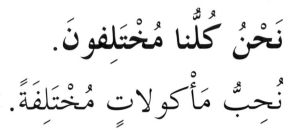

نَحْنُ كُلُّنا مُخْتَلِفونَ.
نُحِبُّ مَأْكولاتٍ مُخْتَلِفَةً.

ماذا تُحِبُّ أَنْ تَأْكُلَ؟
ماذا تَكْرَهُ أَنْ تَأْكُلَ؟

نَحْنُ كُلُّنا مُتَشابِهونَ.
كُلُّنا يُحِبُّ أَنْ يَلْعَبَ.

نَحْنُ كُلُّنا مُخْتَلِفونَ.

بَعْضُنا يُحِبُّ أَنْ يُمَثِّلَ.

بَعْضُنا يُحِبُّ أَنْ يَتَسَلَّقَ.

بَعْضُنا يُحِبُّ أَنْ يَقْرَأَ.

وَبَعْضُنا يُحِبُّ أَنْ يَلْعَبَ بِالْكُرَةِ.

ماذا تُحِبُّ أَنْ تَفْعَلَ؟

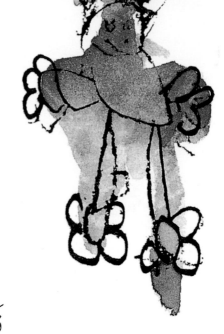

نَحْنُ كُلُّنا مُتَشابِهونَ.
نَحْنُ كُلُّنا مُخْتَلِفونَ.

How to Use the Samples in This Book

The writing models and lessons in this book are not intended to replace discussions centered around published writing, peer critiques, or teacher conferences. Instead, they may be used as a supplement to enhance students' understanding of specific craft elements—an understanding that will in turn strengthen student writing. Each mini-lesson focuses on a writing skill and provides teaching strategies for using the writing samples related to this skill. You can use the samples and mini-lesson ideas to

1. introduce a new craft element to your students.

2. reinforce efforts you've seen your students make.

3. nudge students into revision with one craft element in mind.

The anonymity of the writing samples ensures a safe, comfortable environment for discussing the quality of the writing. Children aren't worried that their writing, with or without name, will suddenly appear in front of the class. After you see the power of these kinds of pieces, you can generate additional examples for your students to critique.

I have found the greatest results when I reuse the same samples within a short time frame. I recommend using one set of samples and related mini-lessons for at least two weeks before introducing another craft element. We want children to identify, apply, practice, and recognize each writing element before adding another. For instance, if I'm working with third graders on show, don't tell, I may introduce the craft element with the writing sample set from Chapter 6 on the interactive whiteboard and guide children to discover which sample has more show than tell. A few days later, when students are moving into peer conferences and revision, I'll place those same samples on the whiteboard and lead them through a discussion so they can again identify how to add show to their writing. Now that students are emotionally involved in their own pieces, they are more likely to reexamine their writing with a critical eye to find opportunities where they can use these strategies.

We teach the tools of writing so children will be able to communicate more effectively. Our main goal always remains to provide the strategies and skills that enable every student to express his or her thoughts and ideas. Use these samples to enhance your students' understanding of the craft of writing. Then, step back and encourage them to take risks and write boldly about what they know and feel.

Meaning

1

She did it again! I was so mad. I told Mom and she said that I need to be kind. She said that my sister is young and just learning about these things. I try to teach her, but she doesn't listen. I say don't do that, but she does. I gently push her out of my room, but she comes right back. Ughhh! My little sister can be such a pest!

Stay Out of My Room! **2**

My sister Rory is always coming into my room. I wish she'd stay out! She opens my drawers and throws my things on the floor. It makes me angry. I tell her to stop and ask her to leave, but she doesn't. When I tell my mom, she makes excuses for Rory. She says she is young and just learning how to behave. Well, I say she'd better learn fast if she ever wants to be good friends!

In this set of writing samples from Chapter 1, both pieces describe an annoying little sister. One sample is written in a vague, confusing way, while the other piece is clearly written and easier to understand. Comparing and contrasting the two samples helps children understand the lesson focus: how writers use specific details to make their writing meaningful to a reader.

Meaning

THE QUESTION TO EXPLORE

Does All of My Writing Make Sense?

Once children select a topic and organize their thoughts, they write quickly. Their enthusiasm for their ideas takes control. Quite often, however, the first draft does not have the clear meaning that was in a writer's mind. Even when children silently reread the piece, they may or may not be able to catch gaps in meaning. Writers tend to fill in missing information with what they know. How can we help student writers check that their writing makes sense?

First we want to get them in the habit of rereading their writing to notice any missing or unnecessary ideas. Reading to the wall is a great strategy to teach your young writers to get them in this habit (see "Read to the Wall" on page 7).

But even reading to the wall will not always help a writer identify lapses in meaning. I explain to students that my husband acts as my first editor. That means he listens to or reads my writing carefully. Sometimes writers are just too close to their own work. That's when it's time to ask a friend: *Does all of my writing make sense?*

Before we ask children to work with a friend on meaning, we need to offer them mini-lessons on this craft element.

Introducing the Craft Element: Meaning

Begin your mini-lesson on meaning like this:

Teacher: When we talk to someone, we want him or her to understand everything we are saying. That's why we speak clearly and loud enough to be heard. It's the same with writing. When we share our work with an audience, we want our listeners or readers to be able to understand what we write. We want all of our writing to make sense. If our writing is confusing, then the audience won't really know what we were trying to say.

Please listen carefully to these sentences: **She wore it all day long, inside and outside. The front curled up and held a large flower, like a peony, made of silk. In the back, ribbons twisted behind her when she walked.**

Now tell me, who am I talking about?

Responses will vary. One student may say I'm talking about a girl. Someone else could say it was a woman. Yet another may say it was a teacher.

Teacher: Could you now tell me what she wore all day long?

Again, answers will vary. One student may say it's a dress. Another may say it's a sweater. Still, someone else may say it's a hat.

Read to the Wall

I encourage student writers to "read to the wall" upon completion of their first drafts. I demonstrate by taking my draft, a folder, and a pencil to the wall. The "wall" can be a classroom wall, a door, the chalkboard, a whiteboard, a hall wall, or even a cabinet. I hold my draft on the surface about a foot in front of my face. Then I read my writing to myself with a voice slightly louder than a whisper. I recommend reading it twice. Often, I will cross out or add words that improve meaning. Sometimes my writer's ear hears repetitions, and I substitute other words for these. I may notice that I don't have a clear antecedent for a pronoun and correct this. Sometimes my thoughts are not complete, so I add more. Children watch, and then we review the steps:

- Take the draft, a writing surface, and a pencil.
- Find an unoccupied space against a flat surface.
- Hold the draft at eye level.
- Read the piece aloud with a soft voice—twice is recommended.
- Make any changes that will improve the meaning of the piece.

As children read aloud, they catch silly errors. They enjoy this brief respite to get out of their seats and move about. But there is a specific purpose and expectation. To increase the effectiveness of this self-check, I ask a few children each day if they made any revisions while reading to the wall. If they answer yes, and they usually do, I ask them to read the passage prior to the revision and again with the revision. (Wow! We're celebrating careful reading and revision!) In the days to come, more and more children find reasons to revise and improve meaning.

Teacher:	Why can't you tell for sure who this is and what she's wearing? Did the author give you all the information you needed? Does it make sense?
Student:	No!
Teacher:	Please listen to these sentences: **The gardener wore her hat all day long, inside and outside. The front curled up and held a large flower, like a peony, made of silk. In the back, ribbons twisted behind her when she walked.** Now tell me everything that you understand from what I said. What do you know?
Student:	We know now that the person wearing the hat is a gardener.
Student:	And we know that she's wearing a hat. It makes sense, since she's a gardener and her hat has a flower on it.
Teacher:	Which set of sentences, the first or the second, made more sense? Which one could you more easily understand?
Student:	The second set.
Teacher:	Why?
Student:	Because we knew who you were talking about and what she was wearing.
Student:	In the first one, we didn't know who she was or what she was wearing. The second one told us.
Teacher:	It helps an audience stay interested and involved when meaning is clear. This year we want to be able to check the meaning in our writing. It's important. We want our audience to know what we're writing. Let's look at some writing and see if its meaning is clear.

TIPS

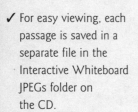

✓ For easy viewing, each passage is saved in a separate file in the Interactive Whiteboard JPEGs folder on the CD.

✓ Use the screen shade or revealer tool to show only specific parts of the passage.

Mini-Lesson: Meaning

Display Meaning sample #1 (page 10) on the interactive whiteboard. Read it aloud with expression, then ask:

- Do you understand what the author has written?

- Are there any words or ideas that are confusing?

- Does it all make sense? Do you have any questions?

If children have difficulty finding the gaps in meaning, you may want to read each sentence independently in sample #1 and again ask one or two of the above questions. Repeat this process for sample #2. After both samples have been read and discussed, ask children: *Which sample is easier to understand? Why?*

If your students need an additional mini-lesson, the next day you can reread the two samples and create a T-chart on the whiteboard that compares the confusing parts with those that carry more meaning. It would look something like this:

Confusing	Easily Understood
no title	"Stay Out of My Room!"
She did it again!	My sister Rory is always coming into my room.
I say don't do that, but she does.	I tell her to stop and ask her to leave, but she doesn't.
She said my sister is young and learning about these things.	She says she is young and just learning how to behave.
no name for sister	use of the name Rory

Discussion Points

If children cannot tell you why they think sample #2 is the stronger piece, ask:
- How did the author first tell us the topic?
- Does the first sentence tell us the who and the what?
- What words or groups of words helped you understand what the author was saying?

Meaning: An Overview of the Craft Element

1. The title helps set up meaning: "Stay Out of My Room!"
2. The lead sentence tells us the who (sister Rory) and the what (always coming into my room).
3. Specific words and phrases add meaning. Sample #2: *Stay out, my room, sister Rory, always coming in to my room, opens my drawers, throws my things on the floor, makes me angry, makes excuses, young, learning how to behave, learn fast, good friends.*

TIPS

✓ Record ideas using a different pen color in each column to create visual contrast.

✓ Save this T-chart in a file with the name Comparing Meaning Chart. You may want to use it again during future mini-lessons on meaning or as a quick tool to initiate revising for meaning in the students' own writing.

TIPS FOR WRITERS

What Can You Do to Make Meaning?

1. Create a title that gives a hint of your topic.
2. Ask yourself if your lead sentence has a who and a what, or at least a what.
3. Read to the wall to check that your writing makes sense.
4. Read your writing to a friend. Ask your friend if he or she understands everything you've written.
5. You and your friend circle any words or groups of words that are confusing.
6. Revise those confusing passages. Reread to your friend and see if he or she now understands.

● ●

1

She did it again! I was so mad. I told Mom and she said that I need to be kind. She said that my sister is young and just learning about these things. I try to teach her, but she doesn't listen. I say don't do that, but she does. I gently push her out of my room, but she comes right back. Ughhh! My little sister can be such a pest!

Stay Out of My Room!   **2**

My sister Rory is always coming into my room. I wish she'd stay out! She opens my drawers and throws my things on the floor. It makes me angry. I tell her to stop and ask her to leave, but she doesn't. When I tell my mom, she makes excuses for Rory. She says she is young and just learning how to behave. Well, I say she'd better learn fast if she ever wants to be good friends!

CHAPTER 2

Focus

THE QUESTION TO EXPLORE

Does All of My Writing Stay on Topic?

Once children have a topic, they mentally organize. That means they select the purpose for their writing and the audience. I always suggest that a student writer make a brief written plan of the main ideas or details that he or she wants to include. This is not a lengthy outline. It is an organized list with a few words (no sentences, please). If a writer has a tentative plan, it is much easier to stay on topic.

Younger writers also enjoy going over their plans with a friend. The listener can ask questions that can help the writer decide what he or she wants to include or what is unnecessary. This give-and-take helps the writer home in on the exact intent of the writing.

Introducing the Craft Element: Focus

• •

Begin your mini-lesson on focus like this:

Teacher: Let's talk about the word *focus*. Pretend you are at a gymnastic meet. Your friend is performing on the parallel bars while others are on the rings, the balance beam, and the mats. How will you focus on your friend? What will you do to make sure you don't miss your friend's performance?

Student responses will vary.

Student: I'll keep my eyes on her.

Student: I won't look at the other gymnasts while she is on the bars.

Student: I'll make sure that all of my attention is on my friend.

Teacher: Excellent. You've just described focus. It means to put all of your attention on one thing. When we write, we want to put all of our attention on our topic. We want to ignore or leave out information or details that are not on that topic. We want our topic and purpose to be clear to the audience.

Mini-Lesson: Focus

Part 1: Staying on Topic in a Personal Narrative

Display Focus sample #1 (page 16) on the interactive whiteboard. Read sample #1 aloud with expression, then ask:

- Do you understand what the author has written?

- Does it make sense?

Since these samples are designed to show only differences in focus, the meaning should be clear. Children will tell you that they understand what the author is saying, even in the sample that is poorly focused. Respond with enthusiasm. *I'm glad the author has achieved one of her goals by making all of her writing understandable. It makes sense!*

Continue with these questions:

- What topic or subject has the author written about?

- How do you know this?

- Does everything in this piece stay on that topic?

- Are there any words or sentences that need to be removed?

- Did the author stay focused in this piece?

Since sample #1 is well written, most children will not find anything to remove and they will agree that this is a focused piece of writing. Now, show sample #2 on the whiteboard. Read it aloud with expression. Again, ask the list of questions above. Children will respond that this author has not remained focused. They will identify phrases like these that need to be removed:

- *I like my blue ones best—the ones with rockets.*

- *I always get new books on Wednesday afternoons when I walk to the library.*

- *It has thousands of books that I can read.*

- *Reading always gives me good dreams.* (This sentence could be considered focused since it brings the reader back to the idea of sleep with the word *dreams*. Allow time for student discussion. In the end, let them know that it is a personal choice.)

- *He's a big dog. Our last dog was tiny . . . and makes these funny, grumbling noises.* (This could be left in the piece without destroying the focus. But some children may want to eliminate it just because it is unnecessary information. Listen to their justifications. Let each student make his or her own decision for this phrase.)

- *He does that whenever he's feeling good.*

If children seem to miss obvious errors in focus, you may decide to read sample #2 again, one sentence at a time. After each sentence, ask: *Does this tell us about his bedtime ritual?*

Another way to help children identify the "unfocused" words or sentences is to mark the words, phrases, or sentences that are "off the focus." Sometimes I do this, but most often I ask children to come to the whiteboard and use a pen to highlight passages that need to be removed.

After you have read and discussed each sample, ask children: *Which piece is more focused?*

Part 2: Staying on Topic in an Information Piece

Display Focus sample #3 (page 17) on the interactive whiteboard. Read it aloud with expression, then ask students the same questions you posed in Part 1 (page 12).

Since sample #3 is well written, most children will not find anything to remove and they will agree that this is a focused piece of writing. Continue the lesson by displaying Focus sample #4 on the interactive whiteboard. Read it aloud with expression and then ask the same questions as with sample #3. Children will find that the author of sample #4 has not remained focused. They will identify these phrases that need to be removed:

> *Snow and ice are both made of water.*
> *. . . just like mountains, rivers, valleys, or continents.*
> *They weigh more than cars, airplanes . . .* (Encourage a discussion over this sentence. Some children will want to remove the entire sentence. Others will say that it's important to know that glaciers weigh more than several buildings. Allow children to make their own personal decision about what fits the focus of this piece.)
> *Glaciers don't move up.*
> *That would be impossible.*
> *. . . that they pick up as they move.* (Most children will want to leave this bit of information because it adds more about the movement of glaciers. A few will want to take it out. Again, encourage discussion, then allow children to make personal decisions.)

If children seem to miss obvious errors in focus, you may decide to read sample #4 again, one sentence at a time, as you did for sample #2. After each sentence, ask: *Does this tell us about glaciers?* Use the pen tool to highlight "unfocused" words or sentences, as shown on page 15. Or have children do so.

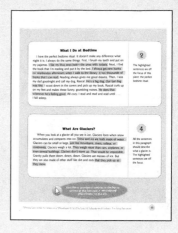

The highlighted lines on page 15 show sentences that are off the focus in samples #2 and #4.

Discussion Points

If children cannot tell you why samples #1 and #3 are more focused, ask these questions while showing one of those pieces on the interactive whiteboard:

- What was the author's topic or subject for this paragraph?
- When did you first know that this was the author's topic?
- Does every sentence have something to do with getting ready for bed (#1) or with glaciers (#3)?

Focus: An Overview of the Craft Element

1. The title gives a clue to the focus. (*"What I Do at Bedtime," "What Are Glaciers?"*)

2. The lead gives the focus. (*I have the perfect bedtime ritual; Glaciers are masses of ice that move slowly.*)

3. Each sentence has something to do with the title and lead sentence.

TIPS FOR WRITERS

What Can You Do to Stay on Topic?

1. Make a brief plan to focus thoughts before writing.
2. Identify the topic or subject that is the focus of your writing.
3. State the topic in the title or the lead sentence(s).
4. Read each sentence and ask, "Is this about my topic?"
5. Ask a friend to read your work and check that all your writing is on topic.
6. You and a friend circle any words or sentences that do not stay on the topic.

What I Do at Bedtime

I have the perfect bedtime ritual. It doesn't make any difference what night it is, I always do the same things. First, I brush my teeth and put on my pajamas. I like my blue ones best—the ones with rockets. Next, I find the book that I'm reading and put it by the bed. I always get new books on Wednesday afternoons when I walk to the library. It has thousands of books that I can read. Reading always gives me good dreams. Then, I kiss my dad goodnight and call my dog, Rascal. He's a big dog. Our last dog was tiny. I scoot down in the covers and pick up my book. Rascal curls up on my feet and makes these funny, grumbling noises. He does that whenever he's feeling good. All cozy, I read and read and read until . . . I fall asleep.

2

The highlighted sentences are off the focus of this piece: the perfect bedtime ritual.

What Are Glaciers?

When you look at a glacier all you see is ice. Glaciers form when snow accumulates and compacts into ice. Snow and ice are both made of water. Glaciers can be small or large, just like mountains, rivers, valleys, or continents. Glaciers weigh a lot. They weigh more than cars, airplanes, or even several buildings. Glaciers don't move up. That would be impossible. Gravity pulls them down, down, down. Glaciers are masses of ice. But they are also made of other stuff like dirt and rock that they pick up as they move.

4

All the sentences in this paragraph should describe what a glacier is. The highlighted sentences are off the focus.

Find these annotated samples in the Focus section of the Interactive Whiteboard JPEGs folder on the CD.

What I Do at Bedtime   1

I have the perfect bedtime ritual. It doesn't make any difference what night it is, I always do the same things. First, I brush my teeth and put on my pajamas. Next, I find the book that I'm reading and put it by the bed. I kiss my dad goodnight, then call my dog, Rascal. Finally, I scoot down in the covers and pick up my book. Rascal curls up on my feet. All cozy, I read and read and read until . . . I fall asleep.

What I Do at Bedtime   2

I have the perfect bedtime ritual. It doesn't make any difference what night it is, I always do the same things. First, I brush my teeth and put on my pajamas. I like my blue ones best—the ones with rockets. Next, I find the book that I'm reading and put it by the bed. I always get new books on Wednesday afternoons when I walk to the library. It has thousands of books that I can read. Reading always gives me good dreams. Then, I kiss my dad goodnight and call my dog, Rascal. He's a big dog. Our last dog was tiny. I scoot down in the covers and pick up my book. Rascal curls up on my feet and makes these funny, grumbling noises. He does that whenever he's feeling good. All cozy, I read and read and read until . . . I fall asleep.

What Are Glaciers?   3

Glaciers are masses of ice that move slowly. They also have small amounts of air, water, and rock. Glaciers form on land when snow accumulates and compacts into ice. These rivers of ice can be as small as a valley between two mountains or as large as a continent, like Antarctica. Glaciers move because of their weight. Gravity is always pulling them down to sea level. Glaciers can grow or shrink. If the temperature is cold and it snows often, glaciers can grow larger. If the temperature is warm, they can melt and become smaller.

What Are Glaciers?   4

When you look at a glacier all you see is ice. Glaciers form when snow accumulates and compacts into ice. Snow and ice are both made of water. Glaciers can be small or large, just like mountains, rivers, valleys, or continents. Glaciers weigh a lot. They weigh more than cars, airplanes, or even several buildings. Glaciers don't move up. That would be impossible. Gravity pulls them down, down, down. Glaciers are masses of ice. But they are also made of other stuff like dirt and rock that they pick up as they move.

CHAPTER 3

Organization

THE QUESTION TO EXPLORE

Does My Writing Have a B, M, M, M, E?

Most writing that takes place in second, third, and fourth grade has a basic organization of beginning, middle, and end. However, when we help children think about their plans and their pieces, it is helpful to say *beginning, middle, middle, middle,* and *end*. That way, we are constantly reinforcing the idea that the middle—the part that includes details and interesting facts—is always the largest of the three. Whether constructing narratives or nonfiction, children need to know how to organize.

Introducing Organization

· ·

Begin your mini-lesson on organization like this:

Teacher: If you were going to make pizza at home, how would you do it?

Student: I'd go to the store and get a pizza mix. And I'd buy some pepperoni and extra cheese. And mushrooms, I like mushrooms.

Teacher: What would you do next?

Student: I'd go home and open the box.

Student: First, I'd read the instructions on the box. That would tell me what to do. I'd lay out all of my pizza stuff on the counter.

Student: I'd get a pizza pan out of the cupboard.

Teacher: So, if I understand all of you, the next step is to get organized in the kitchen.

Student: It's easier that way. And the pizza will turn out better.

Teacher: What would you do next?

Student: I know because I've made one before. You make the dough and put it on the pan. After that, you spread the pizza sauce.

Student: The fun part is putting all the other stuff you like on top of that.

Teacher: Is that all? Is the pizza finished?

Student: No, you have to put it in the oven and cook it.

Teacher: So, what you're saying is that if you do these things in the order you told me, you will end up with a delicious pizza?

Student: That's right.

Teacher: What would happen if we left out the pizza sauce?

Student: It would taste weird.

Teacher: What if we did everything but cook it?

Student: You couldn't eat it. If you did, it wouldn't taste good.

Teacher: What if we used bread for the dough and ketchup for the pizza sauce?

Student: Yuck!

Teacher: So, a pizza needs just the right ingredients and has to be put together in a certain order. Is that correct?

           (*Students nod.*)

Teacher: Writing is a lot like cooking. If you do things in a certain order, you'll end up with an organized story, letter, or information piece. If you leave parts out, or put it together in a different order, it won't really say what you were intending. Let's look at some writing and see if it has all of the parts and says what the author intended.

Mini-Lesson: Organization

Part 1: Organizing a Personal Narrative

Display Organization sample #1 (page 26) on the interactive whiteboard. Read it aloud with expression, then ask:

- Do you understand what the author has written? Does it make sense?

Children will tell you that they understand the writing. Celebrate that fact. Continue with these questions:

- Do the title and first two sentences tell you what the piece is about?
- Do the first two sentences give you the who and what of the writing?
- Did the author give you at least three details or pieces of information after the lead?
- Did the author write an ending that told you what happened? Did the ending sentence or two convince you that you had all the information you needed to understand the writing?

Repeat this process for sample #2 (page 26) and for samples #3 and #4 (page 27) on the whiteboard.

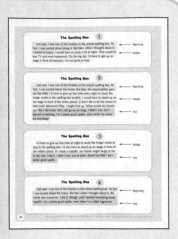

TIPS

After you've read and discussed each sample, ask:

- Which piece has a beginning, or lead, at least three middle details, and an ending that satisfies you, the reader?

At this point, it might help to revisit each of the samples. Using the pen tool, underline in red any sentences that work as the lead or beginning. Change the pen color to blue and underline the three or more pieces of information that make up the middle. Again, change the pen color to green and underline the sentence or sentences that seem to wrap up the piece or satisfy the reader with an ending.

This exercise helps children identify which pieces have a beginning, middle, and end. As another mini-lesson on the same day or the next day, you might create a simple chart on the whiteboard to show what each piece of writing contains.

	Sample #1	Sample #2	Sample #3	Sample #4
B	B	B	—	B
M	2M	3M	3M	—
E	—	E	E	E

Making the chart will be a way to help children identify again which of the four samples has a beginning, at least three middle details, and an ending.

Part 2: Organizing a Story

Story organization varies a bit from the organization of a personal narrative. In a story, the reader needs the character, a bit of setting, and a hint of the problem in the beginning or lead. The middle of the story develops the plot by showing what the character does or how she struggles to solve the problem. The ending offers a resolution to the problem.

Display Organization sample #5 (page 28) on the interactive whiteboard. Read it aloud with expression, then ask:

- Do you understand what the author has written? Does it make sense?

Children will tell you that they do understand the writing. Answer with, *That's good. The author has been able to explain what she wants to say.* Continue with these questions:

- Does this story have a beginning? Do we know who the story is about, where it's happening, and a little bit about the problem?

- Does this story have a middle? Story middles have at least three different actions by the character to solve the problem.

- Does this story have an ending? The ending will offer a solution to the problem and satisfy you, the reader.

Repeat this process for sample #6 (page 28) and for sample #7 (page 29).

After you've read and discussed each sample, ask:

- Which piece has a beginning, or lead, at least three middle actions, and an ending that tells us how the problem was solved?

Again, as in the first mini-lesson, you may want to revisit each piece and color-code the beginnings, middles, and ends. With this activity, the children will determine that sample #5 has a middle with six actions. (An action is defined as something the character *does* to solve the problem.) Sample #5 also has an ending. Sample #6 has a simple beginning, one middle action, and an ending. Sample #7 has a complete beginning (character, setting, and problem), eight middle actions, and a satisfying ending.

Part 3: Organizing a Personal Letter

Writing a letter is entirely different from writing a story or personal narrative. I always tell children to write a "newsy" letter. *Send a letter that you would like to receive and read. Develop the middle of your letter with details.* A letter that is nothing more than a list of questions is fun neither to read nor to respond to. The reader must learn something interesting about the sender. To have a well-developed middle section of a personal letter, the author needs to write three or more details about one specific aspect of his or her life.

Display Organization sample #8 (page 30) on the interactive whiteboard. Read it aloud with expression, then ask:

- Do you understand what Max has written? Does it make sense?

Children will be able to tell you that it all makes sense. Reply with *Good. Max has accomplished one important goal in his writing. It all makes sense.* Continue with these questions:

- Does the letter have a beginning?
- Does the letter have a middle with at least three details on one topic?
- Does the letter have an ending?

Repeat this process for sample #9. After you've read both letters and discussed them, ask:

- Which letter would you like to receive?
- Which letter has a beginning, a middle with at least three details on one topic, and an end?

Children will tell you that it is difficult to tell if sample #8 actually has a beginning or a middle. Throughout the entire letter, the author flip-flops between saying something and asking a question. The letter has a brief ending, simply the last line. They will tell you that sample #9 has a clear beginning with the first three sentences. It has a developed middle with several details; seven of these describe the animals at the author's farmhouse. This letter also has a short ending consisting of just one line.

TIPS

✓ Continue to use the same color scheme for marking beginnings, middles, and ends so that children have a consistent visual reference point.

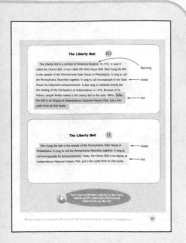

Part 4: Organizing a Nonfiction Piece

When organizing nonfiction, it is necessary that the author establish what he or she is writing about in the beginning or lead. It usually contains a general statement about the topic. The middle will contain at least three details about the topic. The ending will provide new information and also bring the piece to a satisfying close.

Display Organization sample #10 (page 31) on the interactive whiteboard. Read it aloud with expression, then ask:

- Do you understand what the author has written? Does it make sense?

Children will tell you that they understand what the author has written about the Liberty Bell. Celebrate that the author has completed one goal of strong writing. Continue with these questions:

- Does this piece have a beginning that tells you what the writing is about?
- Does this piece have a middle with at least three details about the Liberty Bell?
- Does this piece have an ending that brings it all together and satisfies you, the reader?

Repeat this process for sample #11. It may be helpful at this point to have children identify which sentences in samples #10 and #11 they think make up the beginning. As you marked previous samples, underline these in red. Next, have them identify the details that make up the middle of the writing. Underline these in blue. Ask children to identify the ending and underline that in green. There may be some difference of opinion, so allow time for discussion.

I think it is worthwhile to ask children at this point: *How many details are there in the middle section of sample #10?* Answers will vary from five to six details. You can even have children print a number above the details as they find them. Repeat this process with sample #11. They will find three details in sample #11, but, of course, no beginning.

Ask children which piece they enjoyed reading more. (They will probably appreciate the extra information that sample #10 offers them.) This is a good time to point out that strong writers offer their readers three or more details in the middle section. These are the interesting tidbits that make a reader want to know more and read on.

Discussion Points

If children cannot explain why they think samples #2, #7, #9, and #10 have the strongest organization, place those samples on the whiteboard again and ask:

- Can you find a beginning? Read it aloud, please.
- Can you find a middle? Read it aloud, please.
- How many details are in the middle? Let's count them together.
- Can you find an ending? Read it aloud, please.

The highlighted sections on page 25 show which version of the nonfiction paragraph "The Liberty Bell" has a complete B,M,M,M,E structure.

- Does this piece have a B, M, M, M, and E? Is it organized well?

Organization: An Overview of the Craft Element

1. The beginning of a personal narrative or nonfiction essay introduces the who and what, or the topic of the writing. (*finalist—spelling bee, Liberty Bell—symbol of freedom*) The beginning of a story introduces the main character, the setting, and a hint of the problem. (*Molly and her puppy Bandit, outside, "Uh-oh! Where's Bandit?"*) The beginning of a letter offers some form of introduction or general information. (*My teacher said that you're going to be my pen pal this year.*)

2. The middle of a personal narrative, nonfiction essay, or a letter will provide the reader with at least three details or pieces of information. The middle of a story will offer the reader at least three actions of the character as he or she tries to solve the problem. (See samples #2 and #10 on pages 24–25.)

3. The ending of a personal narrative or nonfiction essay wraps up the piece and satisfies the reader. (*But I did study and I did go up on stage. I didn't win, but I learned something. I'm a pretty good speller, even when my knees are knocking! Today, the bell is on display at Independence National Historic Park, just a few yards from its first home.*) The ending of a story provides the solution to the problem and satisfies the reader. (*"Come on, Bandit," said Molly, walking toward her dog. "I think we've had enough outside games for one day." And she picked up her puppy and carried him home.*) The ending of a letter usually encourages the reader to mail a letter back or answer some questions. (*I hope that you write back soon. Your new friend, Max Weber*)

TIPS FOR WRITERS

What Can You Do to Organize Your Writing?

1. Organize ideas with a brief plan before you write.

2. Reread your piece and make sure you have a beginning.

3. Reread your piece and make sure you have a middle with at least three details, pieces of information, or actions of a character.

4. Reread your piece and make sure you have a satisfying ending that pulls your piece together.

5. Ask a friend to help you find and identify your B, M, M, M, and E.

6. If you're missing something, revise to complete your writing.

The Spelling Bee 1

Last year, I was one of the finalists in the school spelling bee. At first, I was excited about doing it. But later, when I thought about it, I started to worry. I would have to study a lot at night. That would be less TV and more homework. On the big day, I'd have to get up on stage in front of everyone. I'm not good at that.

← *Beginning*

← *Middle*

The Spelling Bee 2

Last year, I was one of the finalists in the school spelling bee. At first, I was excited about the honor. But later, the responsibility gave me the chills. I'd have to give up free time every night to study the longer words in the spelling bee booklet. I would have to stand up on the stage in front of the entire school. (I don't like to be the center of that much attention!) Plus, I might flub up. What would my friends say? But I did study and I did go up on stage. I didn't win, but I learned something. I'm a pretty good speller, even when my knees are knocking!

← *Beginning*

← *Middle*

← *End*

The Spelling Bee 3

I'd have to give up free time at night to study the longer words to stay in the spelling bee. I'd also have to stand up on stage in front of the whole school. If I made a mistake, my friends might laugh at me. In the end, I did it. I didn't win, but at least I found out that I am a pretty good speller.

← *Middle*

← *End*

The Spelling Bee 4

Last year I was one of the finalists in the school spelling bee. At first I was excited about the honor. But later when I thought about it, the whole idea scared me. I did it, though, and I learned something about myself—I'm a pretty good speller, even when I'm a little frightened.

← *Beginning*

← *End*

The Liberty Bell   10

The Liberty Bell is a symbol of American freedom. In 1752, it wasn't called the Liberty Bell, it was called the State House Bell. Men hung the bell in the steeple of the Pennsylvania State House in Philadelphia. It rang to call the Pennsylvania Assembly together. It rang to call townspeople to the State House for important announcements. It also rang to celebrate events like the reading of the Declaration of Independence in 1776. Because of its history, people finally named it the Liberty Bell in the early 1800s. Today, the bell is on display at Independence National Historic Park, just a few yards from its first home.

Beginning

Middle

End

The Liberty Bell 11

Men hung the bell in the steeple of the Pennsylvania State House in Philadelphia. It rang to call the Pennsylvania Assembly together. It rang to call townspeople for announcements. Today, the Liberty Bell is on display at Independence National Historic Park, just a few yards from its first home.

Middle

End

Find these annotated samples in the Organization section of the Interactive Whiteboard JPEGs folder on the CD.

The Spelling Bee   1

Last year, I was one of the finalists in the school spelling bee. At first, I was excited about doing it. But later, when I thought about it, I started to worry. I would have to study a lot at night. That would be less TV and more homework. On the big day, I'd have to get up on stage in front of everyone. I'm not good at that.

The Spelling Bee   2

Last year, I was one of the finalists in the school spelling bee. At first, I was excited about the honor. But later, the responsibility gave me the chills. I'd have to give up free time every night to study the longer words in the spelling bee booklet. I would have to stand up on the stage in front of the entire school. (I don't like to be the center of that much attention!) Plus, I might flub up. What would my friends say? But I did study and I did go up on stage. I didn't win, but I learned something. I'm a pretty good speller, even when my knees are knocking!

The Spelling Bee   3

I'd have to give up free time at night to study the longer words to stay in the spelling bee. I'd also have to stand up on stage in front of the whole school. If I made a mistake, my friends might laugh at me. In the end, I did it. I didn't win, but at least I found out that I am a pretty good speller.

The Spelling Bee   4

Last year I was one of the finalists in the school spelling bee. At first I was excited about the honor. But later when I thought about it, the whole idea scared me. I did it, though and I learned something about myself—I'm a pretty good speller, even when I'm a little frightened.

Molly's Lost Puppy 5

Molly couldn't find her dog, Bandit. She looked under the porch. She searched behind the garbage cans. She peeked inside the bushes. No Bandit!

Molly heard a bark next door. She looked into the neighbor's yard. Molly saw two sets of small paw prints in the snow. Molly followed them. She found Bandit near a walnut tree.

"Come on, Bandit," said Molly. "I think we've had enough outside games for one day." And she picked up her puppy and carried him home.

Molly's Lost Puppy 6

Molly lost her dog outside. She looked and looked for him. Later, she found him. He was chasing a squirrel. When the squirrel ran up a tree, Molly picked up Bandit and brought him back home.

Writing Lessons for the Interactive Whiteboard © 2010 by Lola M. Schaefer & Scholastic Teaching Resources

Molly's Lost Puppy 7

One snowy day, Molly and her puppy, Bandit, played outside. They ran and slid. They jumped and chased. They played hide-and-seek. "Uh-oh!" said Molly. "Where's Bandit?"

She peered under the porch. No Bandit! She searched behind the garbage cans. No Bandit! She peeked inside the bushes. Still no Bandit!

"Bandit," called Molly. "Where are you?"

Molly heard a bark next door. She looked in the neighbor's yard. She didn't see Bandit, but she saw two sets of small paw prints in the snow. Molly followed them. The paw prints led her through two more yards, around a pond and to a big walnut tree. Molly watched a squirrel run up the tree and Bandit bark and jump against the tree.

"Come on, Bandit," said Molly, walking toward her dog. "I think we've had enough outside games for one day." And she picked up her puppy and carried him home.

October 14, 2011   **8**

Dear Brian,

I've never had a pen pal before. Have you? I live outside Van Wert, Ohio, in a farmhouse. Where do you live? I have a brother and a sister. Do you have any brothers and sisters? My two favorite foods are pizza and ice cream. What are your favorite foods? I'm in 2nd grade. Are you in 2nd grade?

Write back soon.

> Your new friend,
> Max Weber

October 14, 2011   **9**

Dear Brian,

My teacher said that you're going to be my pen pal this year. I see that you live in Texas. I've never been to Texas, so I hope you tell me all about your home and state.

I'm eight years old. I live with my brother, Jason, my sister, Callie, and my mom in a farmhouse outside Van Wert, Ohio. We have a barn, but only a few animals. We have a goat that likes to eat EVERYTHING. His name is Vacuum. We also have six hens. They lay eggs. My job is to collect and wash the eggs every day. And, I have a pony named Peanut. Here is a photograph of me riding my pony.

I hope that you write back soon.

> Your new friend,
> Max Weber

Writing Lessons for the Interactive Whiteboard © 2010 by Lola M. Schaefer & Scholastic Teaching Resources

The Liberty Bell   10

The Liberty Bell is a symbol of American freedom. In 1752, it wasn't called the Liberty Bell, it was called the State House Bell. Men hung the bell in the steeple of the Pennsylvania State House in Philadelphia. It rang to call the Pennsylvania Assembly together. It rang to call townspeople to the State House for important announcements. It also rang to celebrate events like the reading of the Declaration of Independence in 1776. Because of its history, people finally named it the Liberty Bell in the early 1800s. Today, the bell is on display at Independence National Historic Park, just a few yards from its first home.

The Liberty Bell   11

Men hung the bell in the steeple of the Pennsylvania State House in Philadelphia. It rang to call the Pennsylvania Assembly together. It rang to call townspeople for announcements. Today, The Liberty Bell is on display at Independence National Historic Park, just a few yards from its first home.

CHAPTER 4

Vocabulary

THE QUESTION TO EXPLORE

Do My Words Paint Pictures?

Whenever I work with elementary school children, I tell them that writers are wordsmiths. A wordsmith is choosy about the vocabulary he or she uses. A writer always wants to find just the right word to paint a picture in his reader's mind.

Once children become aware of the difference that word choice makes in a piece, they notice rich vocabulary everywhere. They hear great words in their Read Alouds. They notice new vocabulary in their silent reading. Many children enjoy keeping a few pages in the back of their writer's notebooks as a collection spot for these words. They write the word and sometimes its meaning. Or they write the sentence or passage that contained the new word. As student writers incorporate this rich vocabulary, their writing improves. Not only does the teacher comment on the quality of their writing, but their peers do as well.

Introducing the Craft Element: Vocabulary

• •

Begin your mini-lesson on vocabulary like this:

Teacher: Please shut your eyes and tell me what you see when I say the word *eat*.

Student answers will vary. Possible answers include *gulp, taste, bite, crunch, swallow,* and *chew*.

Teacher: Please shut your eyes again and think of what you see when I say the word *boy*. What do you see?

Something to Think About

Sometimes children think that the more adjectives and adverbs they use, the more complete a picture they paint with words. Actually, it's the verbs that help readers see the action. Help your students expand their working repertoire of verbs by introducing one a week. These action words should be words that they can easily understand and employ in their daily speech and writing. During the week include the word as many times as you can in your own speaking and writing to bring attention to its meaning and use. Here is a short list of great verbs to introduce to second-, third-, and fourth-grade students:

> *advance, broil, construct, dart, discover, dissolve, escape, haul, jangle, kindle, mimic, peer, produce, raze, shimmer, slouch, soothe, straggle, wither*

Student answers will vary. Possible answers include *toddler, baby, teenager, Pete, student, babysitter, neighbor,* and *older brother.*

Teacher: Now, please shut your eyes again and think of what you see when I say *My baby brother nibbled the bread.*

Student answers will describe the approximate age of the baby and the way a baby's mouth moves as he nibbles food. You might ask a child to act out nibbling, so that everyone can agree on what they saw in their minds.

The purpose of this short exercise is to help children discover that precise vocabulary calls up a specific image in the mind of the reader or listener. Children quickly recognize that general terms are too vague to paint pictures.

Teacher: This year, we want to be careful about the words we use when writing and speaking. We want to select words that will give our audience the same picture that is in our minds.

Mini-Lesson: Vocabulary

Display Vocabulary sample #1 (page 37) on the interactive whiteboard. Read it aloud with expression, then ask:

- Do you understand what the author has written? Does it make sense?

When children respond that they do understand what the author has written, celebrate. *How wonderful that the author achieved his first goal—to make her writing carry meaning.* Continue with these questions:

- Which words or groups of words in this piece paint pictures in your mind?

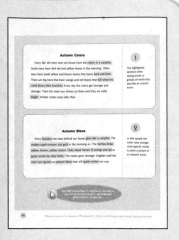

The highlighted words and phrases on page 36 compare the use of strong vocabulary in the two Vocabulary samples.

TIPS

✓ Save samples with the marked sections in a folder with the name Marked Vocabulary Samples. Use these for future mini-lessons on using stong vocabulary.

✓ Annotated samples are also included in the Vocabulary section of the Interactive Whiteboard JPEGs folder on the CD.

• Which image is your favorite? Why?

Repeat this process for sample #2. After both samples have been read and discussed, ask children:

• Which sample paints the best pictures in your mind? Which has more specific vocabulary?

If children are having a difficult time comparing the two pieces, ask them to come to the interactive whiteboard and use a pen to circle or highlight strong words or groups of words. This exercise will help them see the difference between the two pieces.

Discussion Points

If children are still having a difficult time explaining why sample #2 is the stronger piece, display the samples again and ask:

• What are the exciting verbs (action words) that this author uses? (*glow, spark, flicker, shoot, fan, grow, ignites, guide*)

• What are the specific kinds of trees that this author mentions? (*maples, birches, oaks*)

• What are some other specific words that paint pictures in your mind? (*campfire, crimson and gold, gusty winds, noon sun, autumn blaze*)

• Would you rather write like sample #1 or #2? Why?

Vocabulary: An Overview of the Craft Element

1. Use specific names of months, people, streets, mountains, trees, or oceans. (*October, maples, birches, oaks*)

2. Use specific verbs that paint pictures in the reader's mind. (*glows, spark, flicker, shoot, fan, grow, ignites, guide*)

3. Try to use similes or metaphors. (*glows like a campfire, oaks shoot flames of orange and red, noon sun ignites an autumn blaze, that will guide winter our way*)

TIPS FOR WRITERS

What Can You Do to Paint Pictures With Words?

1. Build a collection of new and interesting words.
2. Use a dictionary or thesaurus to learn more-specific words for general words.
3. Ask a friend to help you find the five strongest words in your piece.
4. During revision, substitute stronger words for weaker ones.
5. Ask a friend which words or groups of words paint a picture in his or her mind.

Listening With a "Writer's Ear"

❋

Raise your students' awareness of vocabulary by teaching them to listen with a writer's ear to descriptive passages from favorite children's literature. Always use a two- or three-page selection of text from a book that the children already have heard. That way, their attention can be focused on absorbing vocabulary and phrases, rather than on hearing the story for the first time. My favorite book for teaching children to listen with a writer's ear is George Ella Lyon's *Weaving the Rainbow*.

Teacher: Today, I'm going to read you a few pages from a book we know well—*Weaving the Rainbow* by George Ella Lyon. I would like you to shut your eyes and listen with your "writer's ear" for words or groups of words that paint pictures in your mind. Are you ready?

Standing at her fence, the weaver sees rainbow sheep grazing in her pasture. It is spring now. It is shearing time. When they were born a year ago in the dark barn on cold March nights, when the weaver watched their mothers lick them clean for the first time, their coats were white. And they were white when she turned them out into April fields.

What words did you hear that painted pictures?

Children will reply with some of these: *standing at her fence, rainbow sheep, grazing in her pasture, spring, shearing time, on cold March nights, mothers lick them clean, coats were white, she turned them out, April fields.*

Teacher: You were listening and thinking sharply. Tell me, is there one phrase more than others that you like?

Student: *Rainbow sheep.*

Student: *Their mothers lick them clean.*

Teacher: Why did you select those two?

Student: *Rainbow sheep* is something I've never heard. I want to know why the author used those words. *Rainbow sheep* sounds like they will be different colors, but so far they're only white.

Student: I like the picture I see of the mother sheep licking their lambs clean at birth. I can see that happening. It paints a really strong picture.

Teacher: Let's add those two groups of words to our Lovely Language collection. Who knows! Those words may inspire some of you during our writing time today.

Literature Links

In the library you can find many books with rich vocabulary. Here are a few to share with your students. Have fun listening with your writer's ears.

Weaving the Rainbow
by George Ella Lyon

Dandelions
by Eve Bunting

Canoe Days
by Gary Paulsen

Miss Rumphius
by Barbara Cooney

Letting Swift River Go
by Jane Yolen

The Firekeeper's Son
by Linda Sue Park

Autumn Colors

Every fall, the trees near our house have the colors in a campfire. Some trees have dark red and yellow leaves in the morning. Other trees have small yellow and brown leaves that move back and forth. There are big trees that have orange and red leaves that fall when the wind blows their branches. Every day the colors get stronger and stronger. Then the noon sun shines on them and they are really bright. Winter comes soon after that.

The highlighted sections show strong words or groups of words that describe an autumn scene.

Autumn Blaze

Every October, the trees behind our house glow like a campfire. The maples spark crimson and gold in the morning air. The birches flicker yellow, brown, yellow, brown. Oaks shoot flames of orange and red as gusty winds fan their limbs. The colors grow stronger, brighter until the noon sun ignites an autumn blaze that will guide winter our way.

In this sample the writer uses stronger, more-specific words to paint a picture of an autumn scene.

Find these annotated samples in the Vocabulary section of the Interactive Whiteboard JPEGs folder on the CD.

Autumn Colors   1

Every fall, the trees near our house have the colors in a campfire. Some trees have dark red and yellow leaves in the morning. Other trees have small yellow and brown leaves that move back and forth. There are big trees that have orange and red leaves that fall when the wind blows their branches. Every day the colors get stronger and stronger. Then the noon sun shines on them and they are really bright. Winter comes soon after that.

Autumn Blaze   2

Every October, the trees behind our house glow like a campfire. The maples spark crimson and gold in the morning air. The birches flicker yellow, brown, yellow, brown. Oaks shoot flames of orange and red as gusty winds fan their limbs. The colors grow stronger, brighter until the noon sun ignites an autumn blaze that will guide winter our way.

Details

Is My Writing Interesting?

Details add pizzazz to writing. They can describe setting, show what the character does, explain a scientific process, or set the tone. Katherine Hannigan uses detail to show her character Ida B.'s eagerness to get out of the kitchen and on with her day. "My insides started itching and my feet started hopping, one then the other, because they were ten minutes past being ready to go." Do we want to read on and learn more about Ida B.? You bet!

Rosalyn Schanzer introduces Davy Crockett to us in her tall tale as someone who "could whip ten times his weight in wildcats and drink the Mississippi River dry. He combed his hair with a rake, shaved his beard with an ax, and could run so fast that whenever he went out, the trees had to step aside to keep from getting knocked down." Do we have a real sense of Davy's strength and size after reading these details? Yes, we do.

Details can also enrich nonfiction. In his biography of Thomas Jefferson, James Cross Giblin shares a little-known fact about the newly elected president that shows us his love of nature. "A mockingbird kept Thomas company in his study. He loved to listen to its cheerful songs while he worked. If he had no visitors, he let the bird out of its cage so that it could fly freely around the room. Often it would land on his shoulder and chirp in his ear." Interesting? Absolutely.

Our job is to help children recognize detail, then encourage its use in their writing. I always tell young writers that details provide the reader with something that he or she doesn't already know. It's the juicy tidbit that makes the reader say, "Oh!," "Aaaaaah," or "How fascinating!"

Introducing the Craft Element: Details

Before you show the writing samples on details, have the following discussion with your students.

Teacher: Please listen to this sentence carefully: **The boy went into the crowded store.**

Do you have any questions for me?

Students: Who was the boy? What store was it? How did he go into the store? Why did he go into the store?

Teacher: Good questions. I guess my first sentence didn't give you much detail. Let me try again: **Jeff, a young Red Sox fan, pushed his way into SportsMart, eager to buy one of the twenty autographed bats that had just been delivered.**

Now, can you tell me any details that I added to make this sentence more interesting?

Student: We know that the boy's name is Jeff. He's a Red Sox fan.

Student: We know the name of the store and why he wanted to get in there.

Student: We know the store was crowded because he had to push his way in.

Add Details and Meaning

Children enjoy revising short, uninteresting sentences. Here are five sentences that lack detail. You may want to provide one sentence each morning over the course of a week. Ask the children to brainstorm some questions they have about the sentence. Then, ask them to write their own revised, "detail-rich" versions. Provide time for small groups to read and listen to one another's sentences.

> *She tried to stay on her seat, but she couldn't.*
>
> *The smell wasn't a good one.*
>
> *The two of them played a silly game.*
>
> *The cat didn't act happy to see the kitten.*
>
> *The moon looked scary.*

Offering this exercise five days in a row cements the practice. Continue to encourage the use of detail. After writer's workshop time, ask children to share a detail in their writing with which they are especially pleased. The more we practice and celebrate, the more details become part of students' everyday writing.

Teacher: Which sentence is more interesting to you? The first or second?

Student: The second one because we had a lot more information. I didn't really care at all about the boy in the first one. In the second sentence I was hoping that he'd get one.

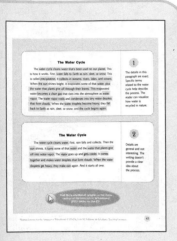

The highlighted words and phrases on page 43 show the amount of specific detail included in the two Details samples.

TIPS

✓ Save samples with the marked sections in a folder with the name Marked Details Samples. Use these for future mini-lessons on writing with specific details in nonfiction pieces.

✓ Annotated samples are also included in the Details section of the Interactive Whiteboard JPEGs folder on the CD.

Mini-Lesson: Details

Part 1: Writing With Details in Nonfiction

Display Details sample #1 (page 44) on the interactive whiteboard. Read sample #1 aloud with expression, then ask:

- Do you understand what the author has written? Does it make sense?

After the children say that they do understand the writing, respond by commenting, *Great! The author has accomplished her first goal. All of her writing makes sense.* Continue by asking these questions:

- Did you read any details in this writing?

- What specific words or groups of words add interest or give you precise information?

Repeat this process with sample #2. Then, ask children which of the two pieces has the more interesting details about the water cycle. At this time, you may ask children to come to the whiteboard and underline the details they mentioned before. With this visual it is easy to decide which sample has more detail. And the details listed in sample #2 are much simpler, using less-specific vocabulary than the details in sample #1.

On another day, you can put the underlined sample #1 back on the whiteboard and look at the kinds of details used in this nonfiction piece. *Water that's been used on our planet* informs the reader that the water cycle is actually recycling water. *Rain, sleet, or snow* shows that the author knows the different forms of precipitation. This sample uses specific terms such as *precipitation, evaporate,* and *condense,* which make the description of the process accurate. The detail *plus the water that plants give off through their leaves* shows that the author again has done some research on this topic to be thorough and accurate. *The cycle begins again* informs the reader that this is an ongoing natural cycle that repeats itself continually.

Part 2: Writing With Details in Fiction

Display Details sample #3 (page 45) on the interactive whiteboard. Read it aloud with expression, then ask:

- Do you understand what the author has written? Does it make sense?

Scholastic Teaching Resources   *Writing Lessons for the Interactive Whiteboard*

After the children say that they do understand the writing, add, *Isn't it wonderful that the author was able to express himself clearly to an audience!* Continue with these questions:

- Did you notice any details in this writing?
- What specific words or groups of words add interest to this piece of writing?

Repeat the process for the other piece. Afterward, ask the class which piece has more details. Of course, sample #4 has many more details.

If children are not sure which piece has more detail, reread sample #4 sentence by sentence and see if they are able to list these details for you to type and display on screen:

straight up in bed

she held her breath

What's that? she wondered.

She heard swish, swish, swish, like the rustling of a satin skirt

Click, click, clack. Someone or something turned her doorknob.

Emma pulled the quilt up to her face her eyes peeking over the top

Squeak. The rusty door hinge announced a visitor

a small beam of hallway light streamed into her room.

"Who-oo's th-there?" she asked, her voice quavering.

FLUMP! Seventy pounds of golden retriever

bounded on her bed.

"Samson!" exclaimed Emma. "I am so glad to see you!"

After writing this list for children, you can ask them to name their two favorite details. I find children always respond to *FLUMP! Seventy pounds of golden retriever.* See which ones your students enjoyed most.

Discussion Points

If children still cannot tell you why they think sample #4 is the stronger writing, display that sample again and ask these questions:

- Which details describe what Emma heard or saw?
- Which details describe what Emma did?
- Which details describe Samson or what he did?
- What would happen to the writing if we took these details away?

Details: An Overview of the Craft Element

1. Specific vocabulary helps build detail in fiction. (*swish, rustling of a satin skirt, click, clack, quilt, eyes peeking, squeak, door hinge, beam of hallway light, streamed, voice quavering, FLUMP!, golden retriever, bounded, exclaimed*)

2. Describing sounds, sights, smells, tastes, or what a person touches helps build detail. (*swish, click, clack, squeak, beam of hallway light streamed into her room*)

3. Describing how a person or animal moves can create detail. (*sat straight up in bed, pulled the quilt up to her face, golden retriever bounded*)

4. Using specific terms can build details in nonfiction. (*water cycle, planet, precipitation, streams, rivers, lakes, oceans, evaporates, gas, atmosphere, water vapor, condenses, water droplets, clouds, Earth, rain, sleet, snow*)

5. Detail can reflect research and knowledge in nonfiction (*water that's been used on our planet, plus the water that plants give off through their leaves, rises into the atmosphere as water vapor, water vapor cools and condenses into tiny water droplets that form clouds, water droplets become heavy*)

6. Detail in nonfiction adds interest to the topic. (*water that's been used on our planet, plus the water that plants give off through their leaves, rises into the atmosphere as water vapor, water vapor cools and condenses, water droplets become heavy, they fall back to Earth*)

7. Specific verbs add detail in both fiction and nonfiction. (*turned, peeking, announced, streamed, quavering, bounded, exclaimed, cleans, falls, collects, shines, evaporates, rises, cools, condenses, begins*)

TIPS FOR WRITERS

What Can You Do to Add Details to Your Writing?

1. Ask yourself some of these questions as you write:
   - What did it sound, look, taste, smell, or feel like?
   - What is the character thinking or saying?
   - What is the character doing and how?
   - What specific vocabulary can I use for this topic?
2. Ask a friend to read your piece and underline details that made your writing interesting.
3. Ask a friend what else he or she would like to know about your writing.
4. Revise your piece by adding some information or details that your reader requested.

Scholastic Teaching Resources   *Writing Lessons for the Interactive Whiteboard*

The Water Cycle

1

The water cycle cleans water that's been used on our planet. This is how it works. First, water falls to Earth as rain, sleet, or snow. This is called precipitation. It collects in streams, rivers, lakes, and oceans. When the sun shines bright, it evaporates some of that water, plus the water that plants give off through their leaves. This evaporated water becomes a clean gas that rises into the atmosphere as water vapor. The water vapor cools and condenses into tiny water droplets that form clouds. When the water droplets become heavy, they fall back to Earth as rain, sleet, or snow, and the cycle begins again.

The details in this paragraph are exact. Specific terms related to the water cycle help describe the process. The reader can visualize how water is recycled in nature.

The Water Cycle

2

The water cycle cleans water. First, rain falls and collects. Then the sun shines. It turns some of that water and the water that plants give off into water vapor. The vapor goes up and gets cooler. It comes together and makes water droplets that form clouds. When the water droplets get heavy, they make rain again. And it starts all over.

Details are general and not interesting. The writing doesn't provide a clear idea about the process.

Find these annotated samples in the Details section of the Interactive Whiteboard JPEGs folder on the CD.

The Water Cycle   1

The water cycle cleans water that's been used on our planet. This is how it works. First, water falls to Earth as rain, sleet, or snow. This is called precipitation. It collects in streams, rivers, lakes, and oceans. When the sun shines bright, it evaporates some of that water, plus the water that plants give off through their leaves. This evaporated water becomes a clean gas that rises into the atmosphere as water vapor. The water vapor cools and condenses into tiny water droplets that form clouds. When the water droplets become heavy, they fall back to Earth as rain, sleet, or snow, and the cycle begins again.

The Water Cycle   2

The water cycle cleans water. First, rain falls and collects. Then the sun shines. It turns some of that water and the water that plants give off into water vapor. The vapor goes up and gets cooler. It comes together and makes water droplets that form clouds. When the water droplets get heavy, they make rain again. And it starts all over.

Who's There? 3

Emma sat up and listened. *What's that?* she thought. She heard a soft, swishing sound. She knew that her whole family was in bed. It couldn't be one of them. She heard another sound. Emma pulled the covers up. She heard another sound and her door opened. Some light from outside came into her room. "Who-oo's th-there?" she asked. All of a sudden her big dog jumped on the bed. Emma told him that she was glad that it was him.

Who's There? 4

Emma sat straight up in bed. She held her breath and listened. *What's that?* she wondered. She heard *swish, swish, swish,* like the rustling of a satin skirt. She knew that her family had gone to bed hours ago. She was sure they were all asleep. *Click, click, clack.* Someone or something turned her doorknob. Emma pulled the quilt up to her face, her eyes peeking over the top. *Squeak.* The rusty door hinge announced a visitor as a small beam of hallway light streamed into her room. "Who-oo's th-there?" she asked, her voice quavering. *FLUMP!* Seventy pounds of golden retriever bounded onto her bed. "Samson!" exclaimed Emma. "I am so glad to see you!"

CHAPTER 6

Show, Don't Tell

THE QUESTION TO EXPLORE

Does My Writing Show What's Happening?

Make the writing come alive! How do fiction writers do that? They *show* the reader what's happening by what the characters say, what they think, what they do, and how they do it.

When writers show, they create vivid sensory images. Readers can almost smell the bacon frying over the campfire, hear the wind singing in the pines, feel the lamb's soft wool, taste the ripe peach as juice runs down their cheeks, or see the purples and pinks of the sunset across the canyon walls.

When writers *tell*, they report information. It sounds distant and businesslike. In fiction, our focus in this chapter, telling holds the audience back—away from the action. Show, don't tell simply reminds the writer to involve the audience in the writing. Invite them into the action and the sensory details.

We can teach student writers how to show what's happening in their stories and personal narratives. Let's begin.

Introducing the Craft Element: Show, Don't Tell

Begin your mini-lesson on show, don't tell like this:

Teacher: I'd like you to close your eyes and listen to this sentence:

Sarah was excited that she won the award.

Now, who would like to act out what I just said? *Show* me what you saw in your mind.

Different children will volunteer; however, one child may jump up and down. Another may say something. Someone else may just smile wide.

Teacher: I see you all didn't have the same picture in your mind. Close your eyes again and listen to this sentence, please:

> **When the emcee announced that Sarah had just won the art award, she rose from her seat and clapped her hands.**

Now, would anyone like to volunteer to act out this sentence in the role of Sarah? *Show* me what you saw her doing in your mind, please.

Several children will volunteer and each of their mini-dramas will show approximately the same thing. They will stand from a sitting position and clap.

Teacher: I see that this time you all saw about the same thing in your mind. All of your actions were similar. Which sentence, the first or second, gave you the clearest picture of Sarah?

Children will tell you that the second sentence gave a more specific picture.

Teacher: Which sentence *showed* you Sarah's excitement?

Students: The second sentence.

Teacher: Which sentence *told* you that Sarah was excited, but didn't paint a picture?

Students: The first sentence.

Literature Links

Here is a list of books that are jam-packed with "show."

High as a Hawk
by T. A. Barron

Lilly's Purple Plastic Purse
by Kevin Henkes

Koala Lou
by Mem Fox

Ish
by Peter H. Reynolds

Widget
by Lyn Rossiter McFarland

The Giant
by Claire Ewart

More Practice: How to Show, Not Tell

✳

Here are a few more examples for children to act out. After each sentence, ask them if it painted a clear picture in their minds. If it did, it was a good example of "show."

The mother held the baby.	*The mother placed her infant against her shoulder and patted his back.*
Aunt Millie made dinner.	*Aunt Millie mixed the salad with two spoons and buttered the toast.*
Jacob didn't want to go.	*Jacob stood on the bottom step with his hands across his chest, shaking his head no.*

Children also enjoy listening with their writers' ears. Find passages in books that you all know and appreciate. Ask children to listen with their writers' ears for groups of words that show actions, feelings, setting, thoughts, or spoken words. Make a list of three or four examples to keep as a resource for writing time. See page 35 for more ideas about listening with a writer's ear.

Teacher: This year we are going to work on *showing* feelings and *showing* what's happening, rather than just *telling* about it.

When a writer shows what is happening, he or she may
- show what the character does.
- write the exact words a character says.
- write the thoughts of a character.
- use active verbs.
- paint pictures using the five senses.
- show feelings by describing the character's actions.

Mini-Lesson: Show, Don't Tell

Display Show, Don't Tell sample #1 (page 51) on the interactive whiteboard. Read it aloud with expression, then ask:

- Do you understand what the author has written? Does it make sense?

Celebrate the fact that your students do understand the writing: *The writer successfully carried meaning to his audience.* Continue with these questions:

- Do you feel as if you're right there at the ball field, seeing and hearing what's happening?

- Which groups of words *showed* you what the narrator did?

Show the Difference

Offer a reinforcing mini-lesson on show, don't tell like this:

Display the Show, Don't Tell samples #1 and #2 after children have underlined the phrases that "show" on a copy of page 51. Ask them to find some of the "tell" phrases in sample #2. When a student says a phrase like *I missed the ball again,* ask him or her how the author showed that in sample #1. (*Whooosh! "Strike two!" the umpire called.*) Children enjoy this comparison. If someone else mentions *disappointed,* then have the student find the words in sample #1 that show the disappointment. (*hung my head*)'"

You can create a comparison chart with the "tell" statement on the left and the "show" on the right. This is a helpful classroom support as children craft their own pieces.

> **Tell:** All I wanted was a hit.
>
> **Show:** *Just a hit,* I thought, *that's all I want.*

Scholastic Teaching Resources   *Writing Lessons for the Interactive Whiteboard*

- Can you pick one group of words and *show* me what this baseball player did? Did the author *tell* you about the narrator's feelings or did she *show* you?

- Can you give me an example?

Repeat this process, displaying sample #2 on the interactive whiteboard. Then, ask the class which of the two pieces has more "show." At this time, you might ask children to come to the whiteboard and underline the words or groups of words that show in sample #1. Repeat the process for sample #2. After examining both of these pieces, it should be evident to all children that sample #1 has more "show."

Discussion Points

If children cannot tell you why they think sample #1 is the stronger piece, display that sample again and ask:

- Did the writer give us the exact words spoken or thought?
- Did the author tell us how the narrator's body reacted to different feelings?
- Did the author use active verbs and paint pictures of what the narrator does?
- Did the author use any specific words for sounds?

Show, Don't Tell: An Overview of the Craft Element

1. Use active verbs to show what's happening. (*called, stepped, hung, thought, swung, raised, pulled, watched, dropped, ran*)

2. Use the exact words a character spoke. (*"Strike two!" the umpire called.*)

3. Show the feelings of a character by what he does. (*hung his head, heartbeat throbbing in my ears*)

4. Paint pictures with specific words or groups of words. (*I raised the bat over my shoulder and waited, I dropped the bat and ran and ran and ran, first base*)

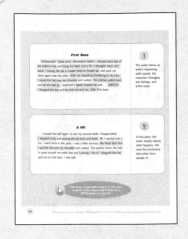

The highlighted words and phrases on page 50 indicate details that show in both samples #1 and #2.

TIPS

✓ Save samples with the marked sections in a folder with the name Marked Show Samples. Use these for future mini-lessons on using stong vocabulary.

✓ Annotated samples are also included in the Show, Don't Tell section of the Interactive Whiteboard JPEGs folder on the CD.

TIPS FOR WRITERS

What Can You Do to Show, Not Tell?

1. Shut your eyes and see what you want to write.

2. Think of what your character would say or think.

3. Write with active verbs.

4. Ask a friend to find words that you wrote that show how the character feels.

5. Ask a friend to find words that you wrote that show what the character does.

6. Ask a friend to find words that you wrote that tell instead of show.

7. Revise your "tell" into "show."

First Base

Whooooosh! "Strike two!" the umpire called. I stepped back out of the batter's box and hung my head. *Just a hit*, I thought, *that's all I want.* I swung the bat a couple times to loosen up, and took my place again near the plate. With my heartbeat throbbing in my ears, I raised the bat over my shoulder and waited. The pitcher pulled back and let the ball fly. I watched it speed toward me and . . . SMACK! I dropped the bat and ran and ran and ran. Safe! First base.

The writer shows us what's happening with sounds, the character's thoughts and feelings, and active verbs.

A Hit

I missed the ball again. It was my second strike. Disappointed, I stepped away and swung the bat back and forth. All I wanted was a hit. I went back to the plate. I was a little nervous. My heart beat fast. I put the bat over my shoulder and waited. The pitcher threw the ball. It came toward me really fast and I swung. I hit it! I dropped the bat and ran to first base. I was safe.

In this piece, the writer mostly reports what happens. We miss the excitement and action from sample #1.

Find these annotated samples in the Show, Don't Tell section of the Interactive Whiteboard JPEGs folder on the CD.

First Base (1)

Whooooosh! "Strike two!" the umpire called. I stepped back out of the batter's box and hung my head. *Just a hit*, I thought, *that's all I want.* I swung the bat a couple times to loosen up, and took my place again near the plate. With my heartbeat throbbing in my ears, I raised the bat over my shoulder and waited. The pitcher pulled back and let the ball fly. I watched it speed toward me and . . . SMACK! I dropped the bat and ran and ran and ran. Safe! First base.

A Hit (2)

I missed the ball again. It was my second strike. Disappointed, I stepped away and swung the bat back and forth. All I wanted was a hit. I went back to the plate. I was a little nervous. My heart beat fast. I put the bat over my shoulder and waited. The pitcher threw the ball. It came toward me really fast and I swung. I hit it! I dropped the bat and ran to first base. I was safe.

CHAPTER 7

Leads

THE QUESTION TO EXPLORE

Do You Want to Read On?

A lead is important. It's the first opportunity for a writer to state his or her intent and to lure the audience into the piece. Of course, we want to help children craft leads that will do both. The best way to start is to study published leads. See what authors include in their leads. Look at style. Some leads are dramatic, some are quiet, and still others are filled with details of setting and character. By examining the work of others, children quickly realize that leads are unique and designed to fit the purpose of the writing. Read. Study. Experiment. Watch the excitement and interest that first lines can generate.

Introducing the Craft Element: Leads

• •

Begin your mini-lesson on leads like this:

Teacher: If you were going to enter a bike race, how would you prepare?

Student: I would practice every day so I was in a good shape.

Student: I'd make sure that everything on my bike was working right.

Student: I'd make sure that I got off to a good start. I'd try to get ahead right away.

Teacher: This year when we're writing, we will do many of those same things. We will practice every day by writing. We will try to make sure that our tools and strategies to create meaning, stay focused,

Better Than "Once Upon a Time"

Have a first-lines discovery day in your classroom. Ask your students to read leads in many different books and decide on their two favorites. Invite them to bring those two books to a First Lines reading. Have children read their found leads. Then, ask them to decide what kind of a lead it is. Encourage children to use their own language to describe the leads. This activity helps guide young writers away from the use of their "same old" leads.

Children may classify a lead as a "grabber." It grabs their attention. They may find another that introduces a character in a way that makes the reader feel as though he or she has met that character in person. They may read a lead that they consider to be a "question" lead—engaging the audience with a challenge right away. Make this a fun and thoughtful sharing time. You may even decide to make a chart of your favorite kinds of leads. If so, write the lead, the title of the book, the author, and the student's descriptive name for the type of lead it is.

select specific words, and use details are in good working order. And just like in the bike race, we'll want to get off to a good start. What can we do to make sure that our leads get our writing off to a good start?

Student: Write leads that are interesting. I don't like boring leads.

Teacher: That's right. An audience wants a lead that is entertaining and informative. We need to let our audience know what we're writing about, but in a way that has some pizzazz. Besides informing the audience, what else should a lead do? Do you want your audience to stop reading after the lead?

Student: No, I'd want them to keep on reading. A lead should make them want to read the whole thing.

Teacher: So our lead needs to attract our readers—make them want more?

Student: Yes.

Teacher: So, let's think about this again. A lead has two jobs. The first job is to—

Student: Give the reader an idea of what the writing is all about—but in an interesting way.

Teacher: And the second job of a lead is to—

Student: Make the audience want to read on.

Teacher: Let's look at some leads and see if they inform, delight, and make us want to read more.

Literature Links

Here are a few narrative titles that offer "promising" leads. By "promising" I mean that the lead suggests to the reader that there will soon be an interesting problem to read about.

Guji Guji
by Chih-Yuan Chen

Ruby Bakes a Cake
by Susan Hill

Owen
by Kevin Henkes

Tippy-Toe Chick, Go!
by George Shannon

Mini-Lesson: Leads

Display Leads sample #1 (page 58) on the interactive whiteboard. Tell your students: *I'm going to read two different leads for the same piece of writing. Listen carefully. Then, I'd like to hear which lead you think is stronger and why.* Read both of the leads aloud and with expression. *Now which lead do you think is better?* Most children will like the first lead better. Their reasons will vary. Some will say they like the vocabulary better in the first lead. Others will say they like the contrast between the last two sentences. Still other children will say it is more interesting than the second one.

A few children may say that they like the second one better because of the words *beautiful* and *pretty*.

Use the screen shading/revealing tool to show only the first lead and ask these questions:

- Does this lead give you an idea of what the writing is about?

- Does this lead make you want to read on?

- Which words or groups of words add interest or grab your attention?

- In your own words, how would you describe this kind of lead?

Repeat the process for each set of sample leads. Of course, opinions will vary among children, but always display the lead that the majority thinks is stronger before asking the questions. Since there are five samples, I would suggest using one or two sets for this mini-lesson and saving the others for another day or two.

These are typical answers to the questions for each set of leads:

Sample #1: Blue sky, bright sun, and the river. Our picnic spot had all the makings for a perfect afternoon. But it wasn't.

What's the writing about?
- The writer is going to tell us about something bad that happened. It was at a picnic spot near a river. It happened one afternoon.

Do you want to read on?
- I do want to read on. I want to know what happened.
- Yeah, I know it will be something pretty important.

What words grabbed you?
- I like the way the writer ended that lead with the words *but it wasn't.*
- I like the way the writer began the lead with the words *blue sky, bright sun, and the river.* It paints a picture of where he was.
- I like the words *perfect afternoon.* I guess because we know it wasn't perfect at all.

How would you describe this lead?

- I'd say this was an "uh-oh" lead. You know the bad news is coming next.
- This could be a "good news, bad news" lead. First you hear what was going great, and then you learn that something happened.

Sample #2: Violet was small for her age. Many people considered her size a drawback, but not Violet.

What's the writing about?

- A girl named Violet.
- She's small, but it doesn't bother her.
- Violet might get to do some special things because she is small.

Do you want to read on?

- Yes, I want to know what she does.
- I'd like to know just how small she is. Is she a fairy?

What words grabbed you?

- *Drawback.*
- I like when it says, *but not Violet.*
- I like the word *considered.*

How would you describe this lead?

- It could be called a "here she is" lead. Like the way people introduce you to someone.
- This could be a "not really" lead. She's small and that could be a drawback, but not really.
- Or maybe we could call it a "fooled you" lead. It makes you think one thing and then tells you something else.

Sample #3: Lightning flashed. Thunder shook the earth. I dove into my sleeping bag and shut my eyes tight.

What's the writing about?

- It sounds like the writer was scared during a thunderstorm.
- The lead shows us a storm and what the writer did.
- I bet the storm is going to get worse and the writer is going to be more frightened.

Do you want to read on?

- Yes. I want to know if he's safe or something else happens.
- I want to know what happens next.
- Maybe a tornado is coming.

What words grabbed you?

- *Lightning* and *thunder*.
- I liked *dove into my sleeping bag*.
- *Thunder shook the earth*. I don't like it when that happens.

How would you describe this lead?

- Big and loud!
- This is a "show" lead. The writer showed us lightning, thunder, and what the writer did.
- I'd call this an "action" lead. A lot happens.

Sample #4: Wheeeeeeee! I zoomed down the waterslide. My legs and arms twisted and turned, flying every which way.

What's the writing about?

- It's about the writer going down a waterslide—fast.
- It's about losing control on a waterslide.
- It's about having fun on a waterslide.

Do you want to read on?

- Yes. I want to know if he does it again.
- Sure. I want to know what happens next.

What words grabbed you?

- *Wheeeeeeee!*
- I liked *wheeeeeeee!* and *zoomed*.
- I like the picture that *flying every which way* paints in my mind.
- *Twisted* and *turned* are good, too.

How would you describe this lead?

- It's an "I was there" lead because the author was at the waterslide and so she can tell us what it was like.
- This could be another "action" lead.

Sample #5: Have you ever done something on a dare? I did. Last year I walked into a haunted house. I wish I hadn't.

What's the writing about?

- The writer walked inside a haunted house and it wasn't a good time.
- Last year the writer went into a haunted house.

Do you want to read on?

- Yes. I want to know what happened in there.
- This is going to be a good story, you can tell.

What words grabbed you?

- *Haunted house.*
- I liked *dare* and *haunted house.*
- I like the last part, *I wish I hadn't.*

How would you describe this lead?

- This is another "uh-oh" lead.
- It could be called a "question" lead since it starts with a question.
- I could name it a "scary" lead, since you know something scary is going to happen.

Discussion Points

If children are still having a difficult time deciding which of the leads is better and why, ask these questions:

- Does this lead give you an idea of the topic? The who or the what?
- Does it also have some interesting details and words?
- Does this lead have some pizzazz?
- Does it sound like the beginning of a piece of writing?

Leads: An Overview of the Craft Element

1. The lead introduces the topic. (the who or the what)
2. A strong lead uses specific vocabulary.
3. A strong lead offers the reader a detail or two.
4. A strong lead lures the reader into the piece.
5. Strong leads offer a little pizzazz and sparkle.

TIPS FOR WRITERS

How Can You Write a Strong Lead?

1. Read many different kinds of leads in books and magazines.
2. Record some of your favorite leads in your writer's notebook.
3. Write more than one lead for your piece and decide which you like best.
4. Paint pictures in your reader's mind with your leads.
5. Check that your lead gives the reader an idea of the topic. (the who or the what)
6. Read your lead to a friend and ask, "Do you want to hear more?"

Leads

1
- Blue sky, bright sun, and the river. Our picnic spot had all the makings for a perfect afternoon. But it wasn't.
- The day was beautiful. Our picnic spot was pretty. Too bad things didn't go well for the rest of the afternoon.

2
- Violet was a little girl. She didn't mind.
- Violet was small for her age. Many people considered her size a drawback, but not Violet.

3
- I saw lightning. I heard thunder, too. I was scared, so I got in my sleeping bag.
- Lightning flashed. Thunder shook the earth. I dove into my sleeping bag and shut my eyes tight.

4
- Wheeeeeeee! I zoomed down the waterslide. My legs and arms twisted and turned, flying every which way.
- I went down the waterslide fast. I couldn't control my arms or legs.

5
- Have you ever done something on a dare? I did. Last year I walked into a haunted house. I wish I hadn't.
- Last year I walked into a haunted house.

Writing Lessons for the Interactive Whiteboard © 2010 by Lola M. Schaefer ∞ Scholastic Teaching Resources

CHAPTER 8

Endings

Is My Reader Satisfied?

And they all lived happily ever after. That's the ending many children tack on to the end of their stories. Why? It's familiar. It satisfies the reader. It's hopeful and brings the story to a natural conclusion. Good reasons, but our students can do better. Once we tell them that the fairy-tale ending only works for fairy tales, they will need strategies to draft a fitting ending for each of their pieces.

Introducing the Craft Element: Endings

• •

Begin your mini-lesson on endings like this:

Teacher: Sometimes we eat a great meal and the final course is dessert. Tell me what you like about dessert, please.

Student: It's yummy.

Student: It's just a little something sweet to end the meal, like pie or a cookie. It usually leaves a good taste in my mouth.

Student: I eat dessert slowly, so I can enjoy every bite.

Teacher: The end of a story, nonfiction piece, or poem needs to be good, too. Those final words will stay with the reader a long time. Besides being written well, an ending must satisfy a reader. What does the word *satisfy* mean?

Student: To make you happy.

Student: To give someone what they need.

Student: The dictionary says it means "to relieve of doubt or question."

Teacher: Exactly. Our endings need to relieve our readers of all doubts or questions they might have. The ending needs to pull everything together so the writing makes sense and completes the purpose for writing. If we do that, our endings will make our readers happy. We will be giving them what they need.

One of you said that dessert leaves a good taste in your mouth. Our endings can do that, too, for our readers. If we take the time to craft a strong ending, our readers will leave the writing with a good feeling. Everything has been wrapped up. The reader will understand what happened and be pleased that he or she took the time to read it.

Let's look at some endings and decide which are stronger.

Mini-Lesson: Endings

Display Endings sample #1 (page 64) on the interactive whiteboard. Tell your students: *I'm going to read two different endings for the same piece of writing. Listen carefully. Then, I'd like to hear which ending you think is stronger and why.*

For sample #1, most children will like the second ending better. Their reasons will vary. Some will say they like that the vocabulary is more specific in the second ending. Others will say that there are more details that give explanations in the second ending.

A few children may say that they like the first ending better because of the final sentence: *He was happy and so was his family.*

Display only the second ending on the interactive whiteboard and ask these questions:

- Does this ending tell what happened at the end?
- Does this ending satisfy you?
- Which words or groups of words add details?
- In your own words, how would you describe this kind of ending?

Repeat the process for each set of sample endings. Of course, opinions will vary among children, but always display the ending that the majority thinks is stronger before asking the questions. Since there are five samples, use just one or two sets for this mini-lesson and save the other endings for another day or two.

These are typical student answers to the questions for each set of endings:

Sample #1: It took a long time and a lot of hard work, but Jacob found his grandfather's pocket watch. He ran to his family and showed them the soot-covered treasure.
The day ended in hugs.

Does it tell what happened?
- Yes. I know that Jacob found the pocket watch.
- And he showed it to his family.
- Everyone was so happy that they hugged.

Does this ending satisfy you?

- Yes. Everything worked out at the end.
- I know that Jacob found the watch and that made everyone happy.

Which words add details?
- *Long time* and *a lot of hard work.*
- *Grandfather's pocket watch.*
- *Ran to his family, soot-covered treasure, ended in hugs.*

How would you describe this ending?
- It's an "everyone was happy" ending.
- It's a "good feeling" ending.
- It's a "whew!" kind of ending.

Sample #2: When spring came, a bit of green poked through the
soil. It grew and grew. I recognized the pointed leaves
of a maple tree. One day, there would be shade again.

What happened at the end?
- The writer saw a maple tree sprout.
- He knew that eventually it would grow into a big shade tree.
- The writer seems happy that he saw the sprout poking through the soil.

Does the ending satisfy you?
- Yes. It seems like everything will be okay now.
- Yes. You can tell this is a good thing that's happening.

Which words add details?
- *Bit of green, poked through the soil.*
- *Pointed leaves of a maple tree, shade again.*

How would you describe this ending?
- It's a "new start" kind of ending.
- It has hope—it's a hopeful ending.
- Sounds like a "back to the beginning" kind of ending.

Sample #3: "Boo!" yelled Opal's brother as he jumped from his
hiding place.
Opal shook. "I'll never try that again," she said. "Never."
"Don't say that I didn't warn you," he said. "I'm the best!"

What happened at the end?
- Opal's brother frightened her.
- Opal decided never to play that game again.
- Her brother is bragging a little.

Does this ending satisfy you?

- Yes. It sounds like Opal learned a lesson.
- Yes. Opal has decided not to do something again.

Which words add details?

- *"Boo!" and jumped from his hiding place.*
- *Opal shook, "I'll never try that again."*
- *"Don't say that I didn't warn you."*
- *"I'm the best."*

How would you describe this ending?

- It's a "talking back and forth" ending.
- It's an "I've learned a lesson" ending.
- It's a "show, don't tell" ending.

Sample #4: "Yeoooow!" screeched the Wolf. And he ran and ran and ran and ran as fast as he could, as far as he could, never to be seen again!

What happened at the end?

- Something scared or hurt the Wolf and he ran away.
- He was never seen again.
- He ran fast and far.

Does this ending satisfy you?

- Yes. It sounds like an ending to a tale.
- Yes. The Wolf was probably mean or bad and someone scared him away.
- Yes. The Wolf won't be a problem anymore.

Which words add details?

- *"Yeoooow!" screeched the Wolf.*
- *He ran and ran and ran and ran.*
- *As fast as he could, as far as he could.*
- *Never to be seen again.*

How would you describe this ending?

- It's a "that will show you" ending.
- I'd say it's a "get out of here" ending.
- Or it could be called a "no more problem" ending.

Sample #5: Small? Yes. Violet was small for her age. But size has nothing to do with courage and friendship.

What happened at the end?

- Violet showed how brave she was.
- She was a good friend.

- It tells us that size isn't all that important.

Does the ending satisfy you?
- Yes. I can tell Violet did something important.
- Yes. It sounds like the ending to an exciting story.
- Yes. It tells us that she was great even though she's small.

Which words add details?
- *Small.*
- *Size has nothing to do with courage and friendship.*

How would you describe this ending?
- It's kind of a "question and answer" ending.
- It says, "This is how it is!"
- It sounds like an important ending.

Discussion Points

If children are still having difficulty saying which of the endings is better and why, ask these questions while displaying one of the strong leads on the whiteboard:
- Does this ending make sense for what you know?
- Does this ending sound like an ending?
- Does this ending sound as if it is pulling the piece together?
- Do you feel that the piece is ending in a good way?

Endings: An Overview of the Craft Element

1. The ending completes the writing.
2. Strong endings use specific vocabulary.
3. Strong endings have a detail or two.
4. Strong endings satisfy the reader.

TIPS FOR WRITERS

How Can You Write a Satisfying Ending?

1. Read many different kinds of endings from books and magazines.
2. Record some of your favorite endings in your writer's notebook.
3. Write two or more endings for your writing and see which one you like best.
4. Check that your ending uses specific vocabulary.
5. Check that your ending has a detail or two.
6. Read your ending to a friend and ask, "Does this ending satisfy you?"

Endings

1
- Everything turned out fine. Jacob found the watch. He was happy and so was his family.

- It took a long time and a lot of hard work, but Jacob found his grandfather's pocket watch. He ran to his family and showed them the soot-covered treasure. The day ended in hugs.

2
- When spring came, a bit of green poked through the soil. It grew and grew. I recognized the pointed leaves of a maple tree. One day, there would be shade again.

- After a while, a little plant came up. It grew and I saw its leaves. It was a maple tree. Good.

3
- "Boo!" yelled Opal's brother as he jumped from his hiding place. Opal shook. "I'll never try that again," she said. "Never." "Don't say that I didn't warn you," he said. "I'm the best!"

- Opal's brother jumped out and scared her. Opal said that she'd never try that again. Her brother said that he was the best.

4
- "Yeoooow!" screeched the Wolf. And he ran and ran and ran and ran as fast as he could, as far as he could, never to be seen again!

- The Wolf yelled and ran away. No one ever saw him again.

5
- Violet was small, it was true. But her size didn't stop her.

- Small? Yes. Violet was small for her age. But size has nothing to do with courage and friendship.

Writing Lessons for the Interactive Whiteboard © 2010 by Lola M. Schaefer & Scholastic Teaching Resources

CHAPTER 9

Revision

THE QUESTION TO EXPLORE

How Can I Improve My Writing?

As they become more selective readers, children want to improve the quality of their own writing, and they need solid strategies to do that. When given a purpose to revisit their work, student writers reread and change general vocabulary to specific, remove tell and add show, rewrite a lead to contain the who and what, or add details for information and interest. To be successful with revision, children need practice and recognition for their effort.

Introducing the Craft Element: Revision

• •

Begin your mini-lesson on revision like this:

Teacher: How many of you visit a relative from time to time? It could be a grandmother or grandfather. You might visit an aunt or uncle? You might even visit an older brother or sister.
(*Many children raise their hands.*)

Student: I go to my grandma's almost once a week.

Student: I see Uncle Tom on the holidays.

Student: My sister just got married, and we visit her new house all the time.

Teacher: You probably know a lot about these relatives' homes. Can you tell me something about their kitchens or their family rooms?

Student: My grandpa has a wood-burning stove in his house.

Student: My sister has a big picture of mountains in her family room.

Student: My aunt has a bunch of quilts.

Teacher: Even though you know their houses pretty well, do you ever notice new things when you visit?
(Many children nod.)

Student: Last time I saw that Grandma has a picture of me in her house.

Student: I found another way to get into the barn at Uncle Tom's.

Student: There's so much stuff at my Aunt Judy's house. I know I haven't seen it all.

Teacher: So, could I say that each time you visit, or revisit, you see the house with new eyes? It's almost like you re-see the furniture and pictures.
(Children nod.)

Teacher: Even though we know our writing well because we authored it, we need to revisit it, too. To improve our writing and make it say exactly what's in our mind, we go back and reread it.

Celebrate Revision

Even our youngest writers can learn that revision makes a difference. One of the best ways to encourage revision is with mini-celebrations. Sometimes teachers ask children to share parts of their pieces or all of their writing in the author's chair. After appreciations are offered for the successes of the writing, another student or the teacher might make a suggestion to improve the writing. Ask the student, *Would you please go back and revise your piece with that suggestion in mind? Let us know when you are ready to share again.*

When the child is ready to share the revision (perhaps on another day), ask him or her to return to the author's chair and read the improved part. Ask the child to read that section prior to the revision first, and then read it with the revision (the before and after). Allow children to show their appreciation for how the piece has been strengthened.

Mini-celebrations work well for any number of revisions:

- replacing frequently used nouns with synonyms or pronouns

- using specific or active verbs instead of general or passive verbs

- rewriting a lead to add more interest and pizzazz

- adding one or two details for information and interest

- adding an ending that satisfies the readers

- removing a word that is unnecessary and overused, like *then, next,* or *and*

- replacing a "tell" statement with one that shows what was said, thought, or done

The more opportunities we can provide children to rewrite *one* specific aspect of their writing and receive appreciation, the quicker we will see a positive attitude toward revision.

Student: I do that all the time.

Student: I like to read it over and see what I've written.

Teacher: When we go back and reread our writing, we do want to notice everything we did well. We might celebrate a strong lead. We might have used specific words. Great! But sometimes it's nice to revisit our work and look for weaknesses we didn't notice the first time.

- Is there anywhere I can *show* instead of *tell*?

- Do I have enough details to paint pictures in my reader's mind?

- Did I really stay focused?

- Did I use one word over and over again?

That's why we revise. Revise means to re-see. We look at our writing in a new way. Let's practice some ways of revisiting our work to re-see what we've written.

Mini-Lesson: Revision

Part 1: Revising for Word Choice

Display Revision sample #1a (page 74) on the interactive whiteboard. Use the screen shading/revealing tool to show only sentence A. Read sentence A aloud with expression, then say: *This sentence doesn't paint a clear picture in my mind. Can you help me think of some specific words for* bird?

Children will respond with names of birds such as *blue jay, cardinal, robin, eagle,* and *ostrich.* Write the bird names to the right of the sentence on the whiteboard. Now say, Went *doesn't tell me how the bird got to the nest. Can you give me some specific verbs that will describe how the bird went?*

Children will respond with verbs such as *flew, waddled, climbed into,* and *swooped into.* Write their verb suggestions on the whiteboard to the right of the sentence. Then model another way of writing this sentence with specific vocabulary. Your sentences might read:

- **The female ostrich ran to the nest and covered her two eggs.**

- **The injured robin fluttered to the nest and fed her young.**

Read your sentences to the group and ask whether these paint a clear picture in their minds.

Ask children to revise sentence A in their notebooks or on a separate sheet of paper with more specific vocabulary. Provide a few moments for small and large group sharing. Always celebrate the specific vocabulary that children have chosen.

Repeat this process for sentences B through E, asking children to brainstorm more specific words for these:

TIPS

✓ To focus on revising a sentence or short section from a passage, use the camera tool to copy the section and paste it into a new page of the file. Students will have plenty of room to add their revisions.

B: *girl* and *dinner*

C: *he*, *box*, and *looked*

D: *man*, *gave*, and *her*

E: *place* and *loud sound*

I would suggest doing one a day for a quick review. Providing this practice builds children's confidence and prepares them to revise their own writing for specific vocabulary.

Sample Writing

Display Revision sample #1b (page 74) on the whiteboard. Read the passage aloud with expression. Then, go back and reread the first sentence. Ask children which words need to be replaced to paint clearer pictures in the reader's mind. Use the pen tool to highlight these words. Repeat this process for each sentence.

Open a new page in the file and have children brainstorm more-specific words that could be used instead of the bland vocabulary. With children watching and listening, rewrite the passage using strong vocabulary. Think aloud so the children can hear a writer's revision process.

Share your completed piece. Ask children to tell you which words paint clear pictures in their minds.

Display the passage and the list of brainstormed words again. Ask children to revise the passage in their journals or on a separate sheet of paper. Remind them to choose specific words.

Provide time for small and large group sharing and celebrations of revision.

Part 2: Revising for Show, Don't Tell

Display Revision sample #2a (page 75) on the interactive whiteboard. Use the screen shading/revealing tool to show only sentence A. Read sentence A aloud with expression, then say: *This sentence tells that she was angry. Can you help me think of a way to show her anger? What does your body do when you are angry?*

Children will respond with: *I stomp my feet. I get red in the face. I shout. I slam my door. I take deep breaths. I squint my eyes and frown. I make fists at my side.*

Write a few of their body movements below the sentence.

Then model another way of writing this sentence with "show." Your revised sentences might look like these:

- **The librarian slammed the book down on the table to get the attention of the rude students.**

- **Amy's mother squinted her eyes and stomped away when she learned that her daughter had lied to her.**

You may first explain that you needed to change the pronoun *her* to a more specific noun like *librarian* or *mother* because you prefer specific vocabulary in all of your writing. Read your sentences to children and ask them if you have done a good job of showing anger. *Can you see these people doing these things?*

Ask children to revise this sentence so it shows anger, instead of telling about it. Provide a few moments for small and large group sharing. Always celebrate the "show" in their writing.

Repeat this process for sentences B through H (find sentences E–H in sample #2b). Asking children to brainstorm "show" for:

B: *told them to stay off his lawn* . . What were his exact words?

C: *the train sounded loud*. . . . . Compare the sound of the train with another loud sound.

D: *made a sound* . . . . What kind of sound? When he opened it, how did he open it?

E: *tiny bug*. . . . . Compare the bug with something else that's small. What kind of bug?

F: *thought about her father* . . . . What were her exact thoughts?

G: *cold, real cold* . . . . Compare with something else that's cold.

H: *held the sign; high*. . . . . How did he hold it? How high? Compare its height with something else.

I would suggest doing one of these revisions each day for a quick review. Practice builds children's confidence and prepares them to revise their own writing so it shows and doesn't tell.

Part 3: Revising for Details

Display Revision sample #3a (page 76) on the interactive whiteboard. Use the screen shading/revealing tool to show only sentence A. Read sentence A aloud with expression, then say: *This sentence doesn't paint a clear picture in my mind. Can you help me think of a detail or two that will describe how the plant leaned?*

Children will respond with: *It's growing toward the light. It's almost falling out of the flowerpot. Its stems are twisted around the birdbath. The sunflower is leaning like a windblown fence post.* (Yes, once in a while a child surprises us!)

Write down some of the children's descriptions below the sentence.

Then model another way of writing this sentence with detail. Your sentences might read like this:

- **The pole bean reached toward the house as if begging someone to pick its harvest.**

- **The marigold leaned crooked in the pot, too weak from thirst to stand straight.**

Read your sentences to children and ask them to identify your details. *Do these paint clear pictures in your minds?*

Repeat this process for sentences B through E, asking children to brainstorm details for:

B: *broke* . . . . Describe how the windows broke.

C: *slipped through my fingers* . . . . . How? or Why?

D: *shone bright* . . . . How did it shine or reflect off objects?

E: *made a mistake* . . . . What kind of mistake? What happened?

I would suggest doing one revision each day for a quick review. Practice builds children's confidence and prepares them to add details to their own writing.

Sample Writing

Display Revision sample #3b on the interactive whiteboard. Read the passage aloud with expression. Then, go back and reread the first sentence. Ask children if the sentence needs more detail. Ask them what kind of detail they think would improve this sentence. Underline the word(s) they feel need more detail. Repeat this process for each sentence. (Not all sentences will need additional detail.)

Open a new page in the file and have children brainstorm details that could be added. With children watching and listening, rewrite the sample using more detail. Think aloud so the children can hear how a writer works. Share your completed piece and ask which of your details they enjoyed.

Display the passage and the list of brainstormed details on the whiteboard. Have children revise the passage themselves in their notebooks or on a separate sheet of paper. Remind them to choose details that will paint pictures in their readers' minds.

Provide time for small and large group sharing and celebrations of revision.

Part 4: Revising B, M, M, M, E

Display Revision sample #4 (page 77) on the interactive whiteboard. Begin the mini-lesson as follows:

Teacher: Remember how personal narratives have a beginning, three or more middle details, and an ending? Today we're going to read this jumbled-up personal narrative and find the beginning, the three or more middle details, and the ending. We will then be able to write the narrative as a clear piece of writing that makes sense. First, let's look at the title. That will give us a clue to what the writing is about.

Read the title aloud to children. Ask them to make some predictions about the topic of the writing.

Teacher: Now, I'm going to read all of these sentences twice. The first time we'll get some sense of the topic. On the second read, I think we will begin to identify which sentences will be part of the beginning, middle, or end.

Read the sentences aloud and with expression. Repeat.

Teacher: What is this writing about?

Student: A kid and her dad are picking things from the garden.

Student: Later, they make soup with the stuff they've picked.

Student: It tells us the different vegetables they pick in the garden.

Student: At the end, they eat their soup.

Teacher: It sounds as if you're beginning to make sense of these sentences. I'm going to read them one more time. I would like you to look for a sentence or two that you think would make a good beginning.

Read the title and sentences again aloud and with expression.

Teacher: Did anyone hear a sentence that might be the beginning?

Children will give you one or two suggestions. Mark a *B* above these choices.

Teacher: What are the three or more details in this piece? What are the narrator and her dad doing?

Student: They are picking the different vegetables.

Teacher: Let's mark those sentences with *M*'s.

Students will call out the sentences with the beans, the onions, the tomatoes, and the potatoes. Mark an M above these choices.

Teacher: You told me earlier that this piece ends with the girl and her father making soup. Tell me which sentences to mark with an *E* for the ending.

Mark an *E* above these suggestions. Open a new page in the file and copy and paste the sentences in a general order from students' choices.

Teacher: Here is a list of the sentences in the order you mentioned. I'm going to leave this up here on the whiteboard. I want each of you to revise this piece of writing the way it makes the most sense for you. I'm going to rewrite it, too. In a few moments we will share our revisions.

After children have completed their writing, display the revised piece (Revision-Anno#4 file) on the whiteboard. Your revision should match the model on page 73.

Be sure to tell the class that you could have listed the vegetables in a different order in the middle and it would still make sense. *Our job is to find the beginning and write it first, the middle details and place them somewhere in the middle, and the ending sentences at the end of the piece.* Provide time for small and large group sharing and celebrations of revision.

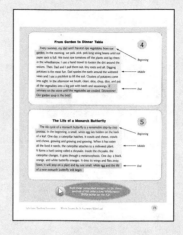

The highlighted samples on page 73 show the correct order of sentences for the fiction and nonfiction paragraphs. They also show the beginning, middle, and end of each paragraph.

TIPS

✓ Save samples with the marked sections in a folder with the name Marked Revision Samples. Use these for future mini-lessons on using stong vocabulary.

✓ Annotated samples are also included in the Revision section of the Interactive Whiteboard JPEGs folder on the CD.

On another day, repeat the above process with Revision sample #5 (page 78). Remind children that nonfiction writing also has a beginning, at least three middle details, and an ending. It will help children succeed if, prior to this lesson, you have read and discussed the life cycle of a monarch butterfly. Display the revised piece shown on page 73 (Revision-Anno#5) on the whiteboard.

Revision: An Overview of the Craft Element

1. Revision is a way to improve the meaning of the writing.
2. Writers replace general words with specific vocabulary to paint pictures in the reader's mind.
3. Writers replace tell with show to engage the reader in the writing.
4. Writers revise by adding details to inform, entertain, or explain.
5. Writers reorganize so that the piece's meaning is clear and understandable.
6. Revision helps a writer notice strengths and weaknesses in the piece.

TIPS FOR WRITERS

How Can You Revise to Make Your Writing Stronger?

1. Read your writing aloud to the wall to notice any weaknesses.
2. Look for general words and replace them with specific vocabulary.
3. Find "tell" statements and replace them with "show" statements.
4. Check that you have details in your writing.
5. Make sure your details paint pictures in the minds of your readers.
6. Identify the beginning, middle (at least three details or pieces of information), and end of your piece.
7. Ask a friend to help you check your piece for vocabulary; show, don't tell; details; and organization. (Just one at a time, please, not all)
8. After you revise, read a portion of your writing to a friend. First, read the writing before the revision. Then, read your writing with the revision. Ask your friend what he or she likes best in the revision. Celebrate!

From Garden to Dinner Table

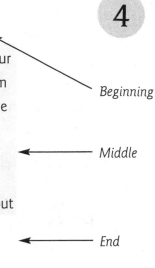

Every summer, my dad and I harvest ripe vegetables from our garden. In the morning, we pick, pick, pick long string beans until our paper sack is full. We twist ripe tomatoes off the plants and lay them in the wheelbarrow. I use a hand trowel to loosen the dirt around the onions. Then, Dad and I pull them out, tiny roots and all. Digging potatoes is the most fun. Dad spades the earth around the withered vines and I use a pitchfork to lift the soil. Clusters of potatoes come into sight. In the afternoon we brush, clean, slice, chop, dice, and put all the vegetables into a big pot with broth and seasonings. It simmers on the stove until the vegetables are cooked. Dinnertime! Our garden soup is the best!

Beginning

Middle

End

The Life of a Monarch Butterfly

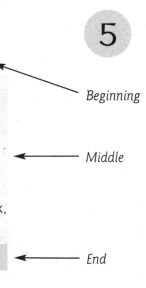

The life cycle of a monarch butterfly is a remarkable step-by-step process. In the beginning, a small, white egg lies hidden on the back of a leaf. One day, a caterpillar hatches. It crawls and chews, crawls and chews, growing and growing and growing. When it has eaten all the food it needs, the caterpillar attaches to a milkweed plant. It forms a hard casing called a chrysalis. Inside the chrysalis, the caterpillar changes. It goes through a metamorphosis. One day, a black, orange, and white butterfly emerges. It dries its wings and flies away. Soon, it will stop on a plant and lay one small, white egg and the life of a new monarch butterfly will begin.

Beginning

Middle

End

Find these annotated samples in the Revision section of the Interactive Whiteboard JPEGs folder on the CD.

Revision: Specific Vocabulary

1a

A: The bird went to the nest.

B: The girl made dinner.

C: He opened the box and looked inside.

D: The man gave it to her.

E: The crowd hurried out of the place when they heard the loud sound.

1b

Passage 1

The girl sat on the bench and looked around. She saw flowers everywhere. Some were tall and red. Others were short and yellow. Some plants moved across the ground with little white flowers. It was pretty. She liked what she saw.

Revision: Show, Don't Tell

2a

A: She was angry.

B: He told them to stay off his lawn.

C: The train sounded loud when it came into the station.

D: The door made a sound when he opened it.

2b

E: The tiny bug crawled on her hand.

F: She thought about her father.

G: It was cold, real cold.

H: The principal held the sign high.

3a

A: The plant leaned to the side.

B: The windows in the tall building broke.

C: The mud slipped through my fingers.

D: The sun shone bright.

E: The clerk made a mistake.

3b

Passage 2: Sea Life

The boy drew a picture. He made an octopus and a sea star and a whale. Then he made a reef. He made the water look blue and white and wild. In the corner he added the mouth of a shark. It was a great picture.

Writing Lessons for the Interactive Whiteboard © 2010 by Lola M. Schaefer ஃ Scholastic Teaching Resources

From Garden to Dinner Table   4

In the morning, we pick, pick, pick long string beans until our paper sack is full.

Every summer, my dad and I harvest ripe vegetables from our garden.

I use a hand trowel to loosen the dirt around the onions.

Then, Dad and I pull them out, tiny roots and all.

In the afternoon we brush, clean, slice, chop, dice, and put all the vegetables into a big pot with broth and seasonings.

It simmers on the stove until the vegetables are cooked.

We twist ripe tomatoes off the plants and lay them in the wheelbarrow.

Dinnertime! Our garden soup is the best!

Digging potatoes is the most fun.

Dad spades the earth around the withered vines and I use a pitchfork to lift the soil.

Clusters of potatoes come into sight.

The Life of a Monarch Butterfly 5

It forms a hard casing called a chrysalis.

One day, a black, orange, and white butterfly emerges.

The life cycle of a monarch butterfly is a remarkable step-by-step process.

When it has eaten all the food it needs, the caterpillar attaches to a milkweed plant.

In the beginning, a small, white egg lies hidden on the back of a leaf.

It dries its wings and flies away.

Soon, it will stop on a plant and lay one small, white egg and the life of a new monarch butterfly will begin.

Inside the chrysalis, the caterpillar changes.

One day, a caterpillar hatches.

It crawls and chews, crawls and chews, growing and growing and growing.

It goes through a metamorphosis.

Writing Lessons for the Interactive Whiteboard © 2010 by Lola M. Schaefer & Scholastic Teaching Resources

Bibliography

Barron, T. A. (2004). *High as a hawk*. New York: Philomel Books.

Bunting, E. (1995). *Dandelions*. San Diego, CA: Harcourt.

Chen, C. Y. (2004). *Guji Guji*. La Jolla, CA: Kane/Miller.

Cooney, B. (1982). *Miss Rumphius*. New York: Viking Penguin.

Ewart, C. (2003). *The giant*. New York: Walker and Company.

Fox, M. (1988). *Koala Lou*. San Diego, CA: Harcourt Brace Jovanovich.

Giblin, J. C. (1994). *Thomas Jefferson: A picture book biography*. New York: Scholastic Inc.

Hannigan, K. (2004). *Ida B . . . and her plans to maximize fun, avoid disaster, and (possibly) save the world*. New York: Greenwillow Books.

Henkes, K. (1996). *Lilly's purple plastic purse*. New York: Greenwillow Books.

Henkes, K. (1993). *Owen*. New York: Greenwillow Books.

Hill, S. (2004). *Ruby bakes a cake*. New York: HarperCollins.

Lyon, G. E. (2004). *Weaving the rainbow*. New York: Atheneum Books for Young Readers.

McFarland, L. R. (2001). *Widget*. New York: Farrar, Straus, and Giroux.

Park, L. S. (2003). *The firekeeper's son*. New York: Clarion Books.

Paulsen, G. (1999). *Canoe days*. New York: Doubleday Books for Young Readers.

Reynolds, P. H. (2004). *Ish*. Cambridge, MA: Candlewick Press.

Schanzer, R. (2001). *Davy Crockett saves the world*. New York: HarperCollins.

Shannon, G. (2003). *Tippy-toe chick, go!* New York: Greenwillow Books.

Yolen, J. (1992). *Letting Swift River go*. Boston: Little, Brown and Company.

Index

Scholastic Teaching Resources   *Writing Lessons for the Interactive Whiteboard*